12.50

KICKING CANVAS

To Dearest Dad

With much love
from Cath & "Lof" 1959.

Battling with the foresail

KICKING CANVAS

by
CAPTAIN A. A. BESTIC

Cadet Edition

LONDON
EVANS BROTHERS LIMITED

© A. A. BESTIC

CADET EDITION – – 1959

Printed in Great Britain by
Cox & Wyman, Ltd., London, Fakenham and Reading
Z.5706

CONTENTS

LIST OF ILLUSTRATIONS

For permission to reproduce copyright photographs in this book the pub-lishers are indebted to *Exclusive News Agency*, *Fox Photos*, and the *Nautical Photo Agency*.

CHAPTER ONE

A SHIFT OF WIND

IT may have been bad steering on the part of Kemp, the stow-away, a shift of wind or the combination of both. The fact remains that the ship was taken aback.

It happened at an awkward time. There was a darkness that seemed almost tangible; sooty vapours of clouds streaming past as low as the mast-heads, the roar of mighty waters hurling themselves brutally over the rail to sweep the main deck with irresistible force and, above all, the deafening thunder of kicking canvas up aloft. We were enclosed in a little mad universe of our own; nothing but tumult, fury—and the ship.

So this was going to sea! I blinked as a ribbon of white-and-blue flame ripped the blackness and struck the mainmast. Standing on the poop, I clung more tightly to the rail.

To windward a big sea with a menacing frothy crest was bearing down on the ship. The main deck was completely obliterated by water racing furiously to and fro with every roll as though convulsed with anger at being confined by the bulwarks; high cascades of spray were shooting upwards over such obstructions as hatches and capstans. To my inexperienced eye, the ship seemed doomed. I could feel the bows rearing upwards, hanging dizzily as though in mid-air, then swooping into a steep valley. Up she rose again, reeled sideways like a wounded beast, and another flash revealed the lee rail under water. With a shudder, she wrested herself upright to roll in the opposite direction.

"Call all hands, Mr. Mate!" The shout came from the Old Man. As Mr. Evans, "Old Jowl" as we called him, stumped towards the break of the poop with his gammy leg and raised his whistle to his walrus moustache, the watch below were appearing aft ready to face their ruthless task for three pounds a month.

They were a good crowd; sailing-ship men, men of the sea who performed their arduous work by instinct rather than by a sense of duty; men who gave their ship a service that was unconditional when she was in need. The kicking canvas had called them before the mate had time to blow his whistle.

A zigzagging streak, whipping down to the sea only a cable distant, revealed their mis-shapen outlines clad in sou'westers and oilskins lashed with rope-yarns at the wrists and ankles. The lashings prevented their oilskins from filling with water. Already it streamed off them as though they had just clambered inboard out of the sea.

Once again the voice of the captain arose above the tumult. "Get those yards trimmed as soon as you can, Mister. I don't want to lose those sails!"

I don't want to lose those sails. . . . Suddenly the significance of the words penetrated my brain. If the ship herself was about to be annihilated, surely the thoughts of the captain would rise above the loss of some square yards of canvas? The words astonished me far more than if the next flash of lightning had revealed him kneeling in prayer on the poop. So far as I could see, prayer was the only recourse left to each and every one of us. Fortunately for the ship and those on board, "Old Jowl" and the crew had different ideas.

Our crew always claimed that not only had our chief mate been born with lungs of leather but that, in some mysterious way, he must have swallowed a megaphone in his youth. "Port watch, lee fore brace! Starboard watch, the main!"

Suddenly the sooty vapours thinned to reveal a sickly-looking moon which seemed to be careering madly through jagged and angry clouds. It was a good omen. "The moon will scoff the wind," was an old sailing-ship saying and, heartened by the feeble gleams, the men plunged into the torrential water. Even as Gogan Lawlor, my fellow first-voyager, and I were preparing to follow them, a hand roughly grasped us each by the shoulder.

It was Mr. Owen, the second mate. "You boys, stop where you are," he commanded curtly, and dexterously sliding down the poop ladder, he disappeared into the turmoil on the main deck.

The braces referred to by "Old Jowl" were the ropes by which the yards could be trimmed in order to catch the wind. The mates slacked away the braces on one side of the ship, and the crew hauled away on the other. Thus the big yards were swung round into the required position. As I watched in the fitful moonlight, it seemed impossible that the men could escape being washed overboard, battered to death, or just mercifully drowned. In little short runs, jumping for the rigging or fiferails like cats chased by a dog, they eventually reached the braces. With weird cries they pulled together. Occasionally there would come a warning bellow from "Old Jowl" on the weather side. "Hang on, everybody!" Immediately the brace would be belayed (secured to a belaying-pin) and the men would literally hang on for their lives. Then would come a preliminary "r-rump!" The big sea which "Old Jowl" had seen roaring out of the darkness would rear itself upwards as it struck the hull, then come thundering aboard to sweep exultingly across the deck. At such moments the men would disappear entirely from my view and, with fear in my heart, I would strain my eyes wondering if I would see any of them again. Suddenly, like swimmers breaking surface after a dive, they would come bobbing up, shaking their heads and spitting out water. Once again the wild cries yelled defiance at the sea.

Foot by foot, the big yards were canted round until finally the wind had filled the sails again.

"Belay, every inch!" bellowed "Old Jowl".

The ship resumed her course. There was no kick from the canvas now, for the sails bellied out, still and unyielding, as though carved from solid wood. The big seas, foaming up under her quarter instead of on her bow, cocked her stern up to rush her pell-mell on their summits like a hunted animal. Between them she would slither down into steep valleys to pause for breath.

"That'll do the watch!" How many times, I wonder, have these welcome words been heard by seamen whose physical endurance has been strained to the utmost after all hands have been on deck for hours on end. At the words of "Old Jowl", the men who should have been below flung themselves, still clad in oilskins, on top of their soggy bed-clothes. Nobody knew how soon there might be another call.

The crisis, for so it appeared to me at the time, was over. To those sailing-ship men, familiar with the sea in all her moods, it was an episode of no more significance than that of somebody on shore putting up an umbrella. They were a good crowd. Seldom has a sailing-ship demanded so much from a crew as the *Denbigh Castle* on this particular voyage. And seldom has Death stood so close to a crew, only to pass them by.

CHAPTER TWO

JOINING THE SHIP

AFTER my father had apprenticed me to a Welsh firm of ship-owners, Robert Thomas & Co., of Liverpool, the real call came in the form of a terse letter announcing that I was to join a three-masted ship named the *Denbigh Castle* at Cardiff. Should I fail to comply with it, my father stood to lose the thirty pounds premium he had paid for my apprenticeship.

Having said good-bye to my parents, I departed with a sea-chest laden with stuff, the half of which I would never require but which the nautical outfitters brazenly declared no seaman could be without. Soon, I stood looking up at the ship with her lofty masts disappearing into an October mist. Squaring my shoulders I climbed up the sloping gangway and walked along the deck towards the stern with what I hoped was a sailor's roll.

"What do you want?"

The voice snapped out of the gloom and, looking around, I saw a man leaning on the rail, smoking a clay pipe. His clothes were decidedly shabby, and he had a big walrus moustache. He moved a step sideways and I saw his stiff leg. He must be the caretaker or somebody like that, I thought. "I'm the new apprentice," I called out, "and I want somebody to get my luggage aboard."

"Well, I'm the mate," answered the man, pausing to spit over the side, "and that means that you say 'Sir' whenever you address me in future, see?" The mate! "What's your name?" he demanded.

"Bestic—er—sir."

"Hum." Next instant he put two fingers in his mouth and blew a shrill whistle. A curtain of dirty canvas which hung over the doorway of a little iron house on the deck shot back, and out tumbled three boys much about my own age. They were all dressed in dungarees. The mate waved his pipe-stem in my direction. "New apprentice," he said. "Help him to get his gear aboard."

Just beside the gangway was a wooden pole or spar with a pulley, or tackle, attached. In a trice my chest was hooked on and hoisted aboard. "Right, lads," said one of the boys, "lift it into the half-deck." The half-deck is the name of the cabin aboard sailing-ships where the apprentices live. I followed my chest into the little iron house which was to be my home for the next three years.

I looked around curiously. It was the width of a railway-carriage and about sixteen feet long. It had four big shelves, or bunks, on each side, and each bunk had a board called a bunk-board to keep the sleeper from falling out when the vessel rolled. There were two more bunks crossways, or thwartships, at the far end. In the bunks were straw mattresses, or "donkeys' breakfasts" as sailors always called them. And that was all, except for a little stove, which was called a bogey, and a smelly cask of water in one corner. There was not room for anything else because the bunks and sea-chests occupied all the space except for a narrow passage, about two feet wide, in the middle of the floor. There was no space for a table or even a chair. Each apprentice "lived" on his sea-chest. He even sat on it to have his meals, holding his plate or his tea-mug as best he could.

We all introduced ourselves. George Hughes and Charles Cowap, of Liverpool, who had already been to sea for two years, and had a further two years to serve in order to complete their apprenticeships. Gogan Lawlor, an ex-"Conway" boy, who,

14

like myself, was a first-voyager. Directly they heard that I was from Dublin, I was told that from now on my name would be Paddy, and so it was for the rest of my apprenticeship.

We all got into our bunks. As I turned over, I could feel the straws of the "donkey's breakfast" sticking into me through my pyjamas, and they seemed a poor protection indeed from the hard bunk-boards beneath them.

"Ah hay! Ahay! Ahay-Y! Tumble out there, tumble out! The sun is shining, the grass is growing, ahay! ahay! ahay! Come along, you sleepers, come along! Arise and shine, you snoring landlubbers!"

I turned slowly over in my bunk, my bones stiff from lying on the straw mattress which seemed to have blended with the hard bunk-boards, and wondered what was happening. Next instant rough hands grasped me by the shoulder and I was rocked violently to and fro. "All awake! All awake!" George was the source of all the commotion. He had had the job of night-watchman, and his duties ended when he called us at half-past five.

The others laughed at me when I started to put on my uniform. "Dungarees are the only clothes that will stand up to the work we have to do today," said Charlie.

The first job we had was to wash down decks. "Where's the hose, George?" I asked.

He grinned. "There's no hose here. We have to pull the water up in a bucket from the dock." And that is how I spent my morning from six o'clock until eight, pulling up bucket after bucket until, by breakfast-time, every bone and muscle in my body ached. I felt as though I could not possibly do any more work for the rest of the day. I have mentioned the word "breakfast". The other apprentices said the meal consisted of porridge and coffee. To me it seemed like bill-poster's paste and muddy water.

At a quarter to nine, the mate had us out again, down the hold this time where we had to sweep up a pile of coal dust and bag it. At noon we came on deck for dinner, looking like niggers. The other chaps called it Irish stew. It was pig-wash.

We spent the afternoon down the hold again shifting heavy anchor chain to make room for cargo. We slaved at this job until it was too dark to do any more. Even then we had to sweep the decks before we got our tea at six.

"What's for tea?" I asked George.

"I think it's curry and rice."

"Good," and I smacked my lips because I was really hungry, "I like curry and rice." On seeing the rice, however, it was so obvious that the rats had been there first that I could not bring myself to eat it.

So ended my first day on board a sailing-ship in port. I was hungry, homesick and miserable and had never felt so tired in all my life. And we had not even left the dock.

The *Denbigh Castle* had taken a cargo of patent fuel on board and we were informed that our destination was Mollendo, a small port in Peru. This meant that the passage would take us round the dreaded Cape Horn.

Of my first sailing day, October 9th, 1908, I have but a hazy recollection. On deck, "Old Jowl", the mate, stamped around on his gammy leg hounding bleary-eyed sailors, forcing into their bemused brains what he wanted done by sheer personality. On shore, dock-masters shouted at the straining tugs which in turn hooted their replies. From the sky, the seagulls wheeled and screamed. At last, the *Denbigh Castle* began to move. I remember standing fascinated as the gap widened between ship and quay. Good-bye old railway wagons, good-bye you dingy warehouses, good-bye. . . .

"Paddy!" The yell from "Old Jowl" made me jump.

"Get for'ard and give a hand with that tow-rope! What do you think you are? A passenger?" I ran.

Not until we were off Lundy Island was there a blast from a pea-whistle followed by a bellow, "Lay aft, all hands!"

"That's 'Old Jowl'," said Charlie. "I expect he and the second mate are going to pick the watches."

We all mustered in front of the poop, the first time I had seen our crew together. Although the *Denbigh Castle* was under the Red Ensign, only four of the men were of an English-speaking race. Two were English; Turner, a naval deserter, and Mathews, the sea-lawyer, always the spokesman whenever complaints had to be made. There was Paddy Fogarty from Cork, an elderly grey-headed man who afterwards taught me all I ever knew about making knots, and finally Taffy Jones, a young chap from the Portmadoc schooners, who was putting in time to qualify for a square-rigged ticket. The rest included German, French, Norwegian, not forgetting the Russian Finn so frequently found at one time or another in almost every sailing-ship.

The division of the crew into watches is always a matter of great interest to the hands. Most of them have already formed a decision between the mate and the second mate. Again, there is often the desire of two men to be in the same watch, eager not to be separated.

"Stand aside where I can see you," ordered "Old Jowl". The picking began. The mate who had first choice pointed towards the Russian Finn, Big Charlie, as he was always called, and Charlie walked across to the port side, after his name had been taken down in the mate's notebook.

"I'll have that one," said Mr. Owen, pointing towards Hans, the Norwegian. Thus the selection went on; those who were chosen by the mate walking across to the port side. Finally came the turn of us boys, and Cowap, Lawlor and myself found ourselves in the second mate's watch. On the whole I was pleased as I imagined the younger, Mr. Owen, would be more human than "Old Jowl".

Throughout the proceedings the Old Man, Captain Evans, remained aloof, pacing the poop leisurely and occasionally glancing around at the weather. He was of medium size with a brown moustache tinged with grey, and rather bloodshot eyes. It was hard indeed to realize that he was only an ordinary man with a wife and children, feeling, no doubt, as homesick as anybody else on board at the prospect of a year at least before he would see his hearth again.

Suddenly the ship began to roll gently and I realized that the tug had altered course to bring the wind, which had been ahead, out on to our starboard beam. A blast from "Old Jowl's" whistle followed by a bellow, "Loose lower topsails", galvanized the crew.

When in port during my off-duty hours I had frequently climbed aloft without experiencing any qualms or giddiness. Being aloft while the ship is steady in dock, however, is very different from when she is at sea. Nevertheless, I ran for the rigging, to be stopped suddenly by Mr. Owen's hand on my shoulder. "Not yet, son," he said. "You'll get your bellyfull of going up aloft before the voyage is out. Just stop on deck and coil the ropes up."

I was sick of the deck, sick of scrubbing it and sweeping it. With envy I watched the men climbing the rigging and laying out along the yards to remove the gaskets of ropes which held the rolled-up sails on the yards. In a matter of minutes the sails burst into big balloons swaying angrily in the wind and occasionally giving a thunderous flap which shook the big steel yard about eighty feet long. Perhaps Mr. Owen was right in keeping me on deck after all.

"Man the sheets there!" yelled "Old Jowl". "Is it farmers

or sailors I have aboard? Jump to it!" The sheets were chains secured to the corners of the sails which passed through wheels in the yard beneath, thence to pass in to the mast and so down to tackles which could be pulled by the men on deck. Presently the struggling canvas was stretched into a contented white contour.

"Loose upper topsails!" came the next order. These sails, just above the lower ones, were attached to yards which travelled up the masts. Normally the halliards or tackles for hoisting these yards are taken to a capstan but, with everybody on deck, they were hoisted by "pulley-haul"—that is by manpower alone—which is quicker. And now I heard my first shanty. As the rope of the tackle was stretched along the deck with all hands holding it, the old sailmaker suddenly started to sing: "As I was awalkin' down Paradise Street . . ." I was astonished and wondered if the poor old chap had suddenly gone off his chump. The next line, however, explained everything: "To be wear-y, blow the man down. . . ." With the words "wear" and "blow", the men leaned back in two hefty pulls, every one of them singing. "A fancy young lady I chanced for to meet. . . ." continued the sailmaker. "Oh give us some time . . . to blow the man down. . . ." sang all hands, pulling on the words "give" and "blow".

So the yard gradually crept up the mast to the story of Sails' adventures with his fancy lady, "Old Jowl" watching its progress until the sail was almost as tight as a board and we could get little more on the halliards. "I thought I heard the chief mate say," sang the sailmaker. "To be wear-y, blow the man down," came from all hands. "Just one more pull, an' then belay." Sails' voice was getting a bit quavery. "Oh, give us some time to blow the man down. . . ."

"Old Jowl" took the hint. "Belay, every inch!" he roared. Four or five young men hung on to the rope near the tackle block. "Up behind!" yelled Sails. The men along the deck let go, and the rope was then firmly secured to the belaying-pin.

Presently there were six straining topsails set, consisting of a lower and an upper topsail on the foremast, and the same on the main- and mizzen-masts. There were also two three-cornered sails on the bowsprit or jib-boom, known as the fore-topmast stay sail and the inner jib. The general term for these particular kinds of sail is "fore-and-afters" (because they point from for'-ard to aft) to distinguish them from the big square sails on the yards.

The next order was the most fascinating of all. It travelled through a megaphone, held by Mr. Owen on the fo'c'sle head, over the darkening sea until it reached the tug-boat ahead. "We—are—letting—go—the tow-rope! Are you ready?"

"Let go the tow-rope, men, and keep your feet clear," snapped "Old Jowl". Next instant the heavy hawser of steel and rope whizzed through the rope lead and splashed into the sea. In the distance we could hear the rattle of the tug's steam winch as the hawser was hove in. The *Denbigh Castle* was free and actually moving through the water under the power of sail. No steam, no motors, no propelling; just the sky and the winds of heaven . . . the endless sea, and the ship.

With the tow-rope safely hove in, the tug-boat made a circle so that she came up alongside us only about ten yards away.

There was one final little ceremony to be performed, the taking of our letters. Charlie had warned me beforehand, and I had my letter for home all ready. A heaving line was thrown to us and along this slender rope our last letters were passed in a small canvas bag. Over eight long months would pass before I was able to post a letter again. As we headed out into the darkness which now lay over the Atlantic, I felt as though the *Denbigh Castle* were a tiny fragment of earth which had broken off, and was now drifting into the unknown.

There was no time, however, to sit and dream. Even after the lower and upper t'gallant sails above the topsails had been set, the decks still remained to be cleared. Everywhere ropes lay in confusion, for the men had hurried from one sail to another and had also been swinging the big yards by their braces, or trimming them to catch the wind. A good hour passed before the decks became neat and tidy. Every rope had to be sorted out and hung in neat coils on its own particular peg, or belaying-pin, so that each one could be immediately found either in daylight or darkness.

The eight to twelve, or first watch, found Cowap, Lawlor and myself on duty. After the decks had been cleared, we went into the half-deck for a smoke. "By the way," said Charlie, "it's your job to ring the bells this watch."

"Ring the bells?" I stammered. "What do I do?"

"The bells are rung to show how many half-hours have passed since the watch began," explained Charlie. "For example, this watch started at eight o'clock tonight. At half-past eight you ring one bell. Nine o'clock, two half-hours have passed so you ring two bells, and so on. By the time midnight comes, eight half-hours have passed, so you ring eight bells. And take care not to be late because midnight is the end of our watch when we turn in, and we turn out again at four in the morning."

The bells play an important part on board ship. Not only do they tell those on duty the time but they are a sort of communication from one end of the ship to the other. The bell I had to ring was on the poop and struck by means of a clapper, with a lanyard attached, inside the bell. Immediately the poop bell was struck, the man on the look-out had to give a similar reply on a bell situated on the fo'c'sle head from where he kept his look-out. He then called out, in a sort of sing-song wail, "A-ll's w-e-ll."

At eight bells, midnight, both watches mustered aft in front of the poop where we were counted to make sure that nobody was asleep or had fallen overboard. "Old Jowl" and Mr. Owen stood on the poop above them. One of the senior hands called out, "The 'ands is aft, sir," whereupon "Old Jowl", after counting them, yelled, "All right, relieve the wheel and look-out."

The longest day, the most wearying day in my whole existence had come to an end.

CHAPTER THREE

THE STOWAWAY

FOUR o'clock in the morning and we mustered to hear "Old Jowl" say, "Relieve the wheel and look-out". At six o'clock I saw my first sunrise. Pink rays suddenly darted skywards in the east, and soon our shadowy sails were transformed into lofty pyramids of pink and gold. The ship ran easily with the wind on her starboard quarter, and the raindrops which had fallen during the night glistened on her from truck to bulwarks.

After we had scrubbed the decks, no water having to be drawn as it was flowing across the decks an inch or so deep from the weather scuppers, we boys spent the rest of the watch making our "rovings". These are plaited rope-yarns, used to secure the sails by their eyelets to the jackstays, or iron rods fitted on the upper sides of the yards.

Suddenly, to everybody's amazement, the small wooden hatch covering the chain-locker was pushed upwards, to fall with a clatter on the deck. An extraordinary scarecrow of a figure emerged and stepped gingerly on to the deck. His face looked chalk-white where it showed beneath the grime and dirt, and his red-rimmed eyes blinked uncertainly. His ragged clothes, stained with mud and rust from the locker, hung loosely on a starved-looking frame. "What's the matter, mates?" His face contorted into a grin. "Have none of youse ever seen a ruddy stowaway before?"

"Aye," replied Big Charlie, first to recover from the surprise.

"I seed plenty but I never seed one on an outward-bound ship before."

"Well, you're seein' one now." The figure wiped the back of his hand across his eyes as though dazed. "A fellah will go anywheres when the porlice are after him. . . ." He took a step forward, then stumbled and fell. "No grub for two days," he explained apologetically. Two of the hands assisted him to his feet and sat him down on a near-by cork fender.

"One of you run aft and tell the second mate," ordered Big Charlie.

"Why were the police after you?" asked Turner.

A look of cunning showed in the man's eyes. "Porlice? Who said anything about the porlice? I'm an honest man, I am," he continued, his voice rising excitedly. "An honest man. An' don't you start . . ."

"All right, all right," said Turner soothingly. "None of my business. I just thought . . ."

"What's all this?" Mr. Owen had come forward and stood looking sternly at the strange figure.

"Says he's a stowaway, sir," exclaimed Turner. "Came out of the chain-locker, he did; says he has had nothing to eat for two days."

"Stowaway, eh?" said Mr. Owen. "You've let yourself in for a spot of trouble, my man. What's your name?"

"Kemp, sir. 'Arry Kemp. I was . . ."

"Never mind that now. You can tell the captain all about it when you see him later. Meanwhile, go and wash yourself."

"What about a bit of grub first, sir, if I may be so bold? Been in the chain-locker for two days. . . ."

"All right, the Peggy will get you something from the cook and bring it along to you here. You can't go into the fo'c'sle in that mess." The Peggy, incidentally, was the man detailed off each week to keep the fo'c'sle clean. He washed the place out each morning and also fetched meals for his shipmates.

We saw Kemp, cleaner but still in his dirty ragged clothes, being escorted aft by Mr. Owen to be interviewed by the captain, that ruler of our miniature world, and we wondered what kind of reception he would be given by the August Presence. Fragments of the interview drifted to us through the cook who in turn had received them from the steward. "Proper dressin' down he gave 'im, I believe," said the cook to Chips, the carpenter, who had slipped into the galley to light a spill. "Told him straight he didn't like the looks of 'im, but signed him on as an ordinary seaman at two-ten a month. If it 'ad been me I'd have made him work his blinkin' passage."

"You forget," replied Chips, having got his clay pipe drawing, "that the Old Man 'as to give him clothes out of the slops an' he wouldn't get paid for them unless the stowaway was gettin' wages."

"True enough, Chippy, true enough," and Cookie stroked his straggly grey beard reflectively. "Aye, there ain't any flies on the Ol' Man."

The *Denbigh Castle* made good progress southwards. As the days passed, the grey and overcast skies became gradually less frequent. White, fleecy clouds, harmless and kindly, took the place of the black rain squalls. "We'll be picking up the Northeast Trades any time now," was a remark frequently heard around the deck.

During the repose of the evening in the six to eight or second dog-watch, the men now frequented the foredeck instead of sitting in the fo'c'sle or lying in their bunks. Fritz and Froggy would be seen walking up and down for about twenty paces chatting amiably, although they fought in open combat at least twice a week, weather permitting, over some trivial matter such as a broom, until Mr. Owen came along and ordered them to get on with their work.

Old Sails, grey-haired and wrinkled, who looked seventy to me although I don't suppose he was more than fifty, often sat with Chips on the forehatch, yarning about their previous ships. Chips was about five feet nothing, conspicuous by a red handle-bar moustache and a fiery temper. He came from Barrow. Sometimes he used to give me lessons in boxing. "Always fight fair, Paddy, always fight fair," and then, after a couple of seconds pause, he would add, "unless you're getting beat. At all costs, never let yourself be beat." Then he would show me some tricks, unheard of in the Queensberry Rules. "They're useful to have up your sleeve." On one occasion I saw him, flourishing a big adze in his hand, chasing a six-foot Swede around the deck. Chips, with blazing eyes, kept yelling, "I'll cut your head off," until finally the Swede, by putting on a spurt, gained enough ground to jump into the main rigging.

At first Kemp used to entertain the crowd with his boastful stories but they soon tired of them, and him.

"Yus, I makes all 'ands come aft with me an' I pushes the plate of rotten grub right under the Old Man's nose. ''Ere,' I says, 'smell that. That's not the sort of food we signed on for.' And when the Old Man says, 'it's good enough for the likes of you,' I 'ups with the plate an' lets 'im 'ave it right across the kisser. I can tell you we got a darned sight better grub from then on.

"The mate? I wasn't long fixin' 'im. Wanted me to wash some soup off the deck I'd spilt on a Sunday, he did. 'Looka here,' I says, 'I only signed on to do work necessary for the navigation of the ship on Sundays.'

"'You get a bucket of water,' he snarls fierce-like, 'and get down on your knees an' scrub that deck.' I gets the bucket of water all right but, instead of scrubbin' the deck, I flings it right over 'im. Laugh? Why, all 'ands were asplittin' their sides. But me an' him, we gets along like brothers after that. He knew what he was up against, see?"

Poor Kemp. In the slums he had found that bluff and lying were the most effective weapons to protect him when he offended against the laws of the civil authorities. Unconsciously he used them now for lack of ideas to express his longings.

Came the North-east Trade winds and, with them, the setting of sail. I heard the upper t'gallant being set during my four to eight morning watch below, the shuffling of feet, the creaking of halliard blocks, the "belay all that," from "Old Jowl". Already I could tell by sound alone exactly what work was being done on deck. Each block, and there were hundreds of them, had its own distinctive rattle, wheeze or whirl: no two were alike, and I could tell the name of each by its particular sound.

When we came on deck, our first job was to loose and set the royals, the smallest but highest sails of all. By now I had become familiar with climbing aloft under ordinary weather conditions. One man could easily loose these sails, and we three apprentices were detailed off, one for each mast. I was given the main, and it was a race between the three of us to be the first to have his sail ready for setting. I was desperately anxious to be the winner and practically ran up the whole distance of 175 feet. Feverishly I unwound the gaskets and then glanced at Charlie on the foremast. Already he was waving his arm to Mr. Owen on deck, signalling that his sail was ready for hoisting. It was only to be expected, of course, as he had added experience through being a second voyager.

I had to wait up aloft until my sail had been hoisted so as to make up the gaskets into coils and also to overhaul the buntlines. These lines were secured to the foot of the sail and, by

27

this means, the foot could be hauled up to the yard from on deck when the sail was being taken in. After the sail was set, the bunt-lines would chafe the sail, if they were not overhauled a foot or so and secured with a piece of twine.

My first impression was that of floating in space above the ship. It was truly a bird's-eye view. The pencil-like hull of the vessel seemed so far below me that I seemed to have no connection with it.

A faint blur appeared on the distant horizon. Even as I looked, it blackened and ascended upwards. Smoke! A steamer about two points on the port bow!

In sail the sight of a steamer meant much more than a ship that merely passes. It was an indirect communication with home, for she would report us to Lloyds who in turn would communicate with our owners. From them our families would receive a postcard, brief but comforting, to say that the *Denbigh Castle* had been sighted in latitude and longitude so and so, and reported all well. Our chronometers, too, could be checked and confirmed for accuracy. A small error in Greenwich Time can make a very large error in obtaining one's position by longitude. Finally, another ship meant something to look at, a break in the monotony of eternal sea and sky.

Cupping my hands to my mouth I turned towards the poop and, with the full strength of my lungs, yelled, " Steamer—two-points on—port bow!"

Hitherto, I had hardly been spoken to by an officer except to be given an order or a "blast" for carelessness. Now, six words from me had affected the whole ship. Mr. Owen gave an acknowledging wave of his arm and ran to the poop to tell the Old Man. He disappeared into the chart-room to emerge with a telescope in his hand, while the watch on deck actually dared to cease work in order to peer over the bulwarks at the horizon. A minute ago I was a nonentity, just one of the boys, and now my name was on everybody's lips. "Young Bestic reports that there's a steamer in sight!" To crown all, I could see by the wake that the *Denbigh Castle* had altered course about two points. For the first time since I had joined the ship I felt a somebody.

"How does she bear now?" The words floated upwards and I looked down to see Mr. Owen standing on the poop with a megaphone.

"Right ahead!" I bellowed.

"Stop up there until you see her hull and let's know how she is heading!" I waved my arm. Presently I could see the white upper-works of the steamer reflected in the sunshine, and a latter examination showed me that she was, indeed, heading directly towards us.

I descended and made my report to Mr. Owen. Charlie and Gogan were already on the poop getting the signal flags ready, and I joined them. The flags were kept in a flag-locker on the poop, each neatly rolled up in its own pigeon-hole. They were in alphabetical order and each pigeon-hole labelled. A simple and systematic arrangement, it worked very well— unless somebody put a flag into the wrong compartment by mistake.

The necessary flags to be hoisted had to be connected by means of a loop and toggle. The two ends of the signal halliards had to be untied and each end hitched to the top and bottom of the hoist respectively. We, of course, had learnt our flags and Mr. Owen had given us a few drillings. We considered that we would make quite a good show when the necessity arose but the Old Man had other ideas. As soon as the signalling started, he kept hounding us all the time. "Come on, come on, get a move on," he kept shouting. "Heavens above, I've never seen such a bunch of butter-fingered young hoboes since I came to sea."

"Don't mind him," whispered Charlie as we bent over the flag-locker. "Always gets fussy when we're signalling." Don't mind him? Why, even Mr. Owen who was looking through the telescope to see what flags the steamer was hoisting, felt the electric tension on the poop.

"What has he up now, Mister?" snapped the Old Man.

"I can't just see for the moment, sir," and Mr. Owen, with legs apart, steadied the telescope against the mizzen stay. "His hoist isn't right up yet."

"Here, give me the glass." The captain snatched it out of Mr. Owen's hands. "Looks as though I've got to do everything myself aboard this ship." He peered through the glass for about half a minute. "X.O.R. Look up X.O.R. in the book, Mr. Owen."

Mr. Owen flicked the pages over deftly. "Thank you, sir," he said.

"Thank you? What the devil are you talking about?"

"X.O.R. means 'thank you', sir."

"Oh, an' why didn't you say so? Here, take this glass," and he stamped across to the signal-book lying on top of the skylight to look up his next signal. "I.T.W., hoist I.T.W. Don't stand there looking at me like a pack of idiots; get the hoist up." We whipped the flags out of their pigeon-holes and started connecting them as quickly as we could. "Hurry," snapped the Old Man. "Do you want the ship to be out of sight before you get those flags up?"

"Make sure the 'I' is on top," whispered Charlie. I grabbed the flag and secured the halliards. "Right," I said, "up she goes." Up shot the fluttering flags, man o' war style, and then came disaster! In my haste I had committed the unforgivable sin afloat, that of making a "slippery hitch". The flags were half-way up to the gaff when the hitch became undone.

In falling, they enveloped the head of the Old Man. As a

finishing touch to our troubles, the now-freed end of the halliards whizzed upwards and, unreeving itself from the gaff-block, descended in neat little coils around the neck and body of our captain.

Escape! That was my first thought, to escape before the bellowing, furious man extricated himself from the tangle of flags and rope. But how? Where? Suddenly I realized that the halliards must be rove off again and that if I were to slip aloft and do so, I would get a few minutes' respite. Untying the end from the bottom of the hoist and making a loop of it over my arm, I sped up the mizzen rigging. Half-way up, and the halliards jerked convulsively as though I had a fish on a line. The unceasing stream of vitriolic language still coming from the Old Man ended in a choking yell. I had forgotten that the coils were still around his neck. As Charlie said to me afterwards, "you nearly pulled his head off."

At last, like mice freeing a lion, Mr. Owen, Charlie and Gogan got him free of the tangle. There the similarity ended, for the lion did not express any gratitude. Instead he sat panting on the seat of the skylight, casting baleful eyes up at me. Next instant he shook his fist and opened his mouth, but no words came. I knew it must be from physical exhaustion as his vocabulary rarely failed him. I edged myself straddle-legged out along the gaff and with trembling hands rerove the offending halliard. Then I came down and stood before him. "I'm sorry, sir."

He sat looking at me in chilled silence which was worse than abuse. What was to be my sentence, I wondered? Stories of offenders on board ship being strung up to the yard-arm, or keel-hauled, floated through my mind. Swallowing visibly, he said, "Get those flags made up and stowed away," and, rising to his feet, he disappeared into the chart-room.

The Old Man was a human being after all. We had not,

however, escaped entirely. Half an hour later Mr. Owen came down to our half-deck and poked his head through the door. "Captain says you boys are to do half an hour signal practice in your watch below every day for a week, and you can count yourselves lucky."

That was the last time I ever made a slippery hitch.

Rolling the sail up on the yard

Heaving up a topsail yard as the long bars fit into the capstan heads

The *Denbigh Castle* lying over to leeward

CHAPTER FOUR

OFF CAPE HORN

I F climbing had been my reason for going to sea, this ambition was more than fulfilled when we ran into fine weather. Then the *Denbigh Castle* had her suit of sails completely changed.

We came out on deck at eight o'clock to be met by Mr. Owen. "You boys go along to the sailmaker. He's waiting for you in his locker." The sail-locker was under the poop and had access to the main deck by an opening about two feet square. At the foot of the opening was a wooden roller to allow the rolled-up sails to be pulled out without becoming damaged.

Old Sails, lord and master of his own particular domain, sat on a bed of rolled-up canvas, legs outstretched and a stain of tobacco-juice at the corner of his mouth. He was a decent old chap and everybody liked him. "Mornin', boys," he said as we climbed in. "We're puttin' up the fine weather sails today and there's a job of work to do here sortin' 'em out. We'll start on the fore t'gallants. Here's the end of it stickin' up." After much straining, heaving and sweating, we had it cleared of its fellows. The watch was lined up outside and, a rope's-end having been passed through to us, we secured it to the clew and gave the signal to haul away. With "yah-hays" and "Yo-hohs" from the men, the big sail departed from the locker like some huge snake leaving its lair.

To my great satisfaction, we were relieved from the sail-locker after two hours and put working on deck. As soon as a sail was stretched out along the deck, we would lift it on to our shoulders, and, not unlike a gigantic caterpillar, stagger along the swaying deck. The sail having been hove up above its particular yard by means of a gant-line, Mr. Owen would shout, "Up aloft and set her, men," and up we'd go, to lay out on each side of the yard. The two outside men would sit straddle-legged at each end and, as the sail was lowered, the ends were passed out to be secured. The rest of us passed the rovings through the eyelets at the head of the sail and around the rail or jack-stay running along the top of the yard. Sheets, clew-lines and bunt-lines had then to be connected, and the sail finally set. In two days the ship was fitted with a complete change which, in view of the fact that she carried eighteen square and eleven fore-and-aft sails, was very good work indeed.

During the changing of these sails my old friend, Paddy, who taught me all my knots and splices, nearly lost his life. He was working on the fore upper topsail-yard at the time (the third yard up) when unaccountably he slipped and fell. Even while he was in the air, somebody yelled, "Man overboard!" By inches his body missed the lower topsail-braces.

It so happened that the foresail was sheeted well home and Paddy actually fell into the belly of it. He paused there momentarily, but the old canvas parted and he fell through the sail into the sea. Fortunately the ship was only making about two knots, and Mr. Owen, standing at the break of the poop, had seen the accident.

It took quick thinking. As though in one movement, he flung about fifteen feet of the main brace over the side and belayed it. Next instant he slid down the rope and arrived at the water's edge just in time to grab Paddy as he floated aft. Paddy, although he had had most of the breath knocked out of him, was able to assist Mr. Owen by holding on to the rope.

We all bundled aft with a rush. There was nobody on deck to

give orders but, as skilled seamen, we knew exactly what to do. "Here, lower me down, Charlie." Already Turner had made a bow-line (loop) out of the end of the topsail brace to sit in and had climbed on to the rail. Charlie lowered him down and somebody else dropped a line to which Turner secured Paddy and up he came, wet and streaming. Mr. Owen climbed up himself, followed by Turner.

Paddy looked around at the men and grinned. "Never came down from aloft so quick before," he said. "It must be younger I'm gettin'."

"Paddy!" The unexpected call made us all look round to see the Old Man leaning on the poop-rail.

"Yes, sir."

"Come aft here."

"Perhaps he's going to give me a glass of rum," said Paddy, *sotto voce* to his shipmates, as he walked towards the break of the poop.

We hung around coiling up the braces again and listening for what the Old Man had to say. "If he gives him a glass of rum," said Turner, "we'll all be fallin' off the yards."

Paddy had reached the break of the poop and stood looking up at the Captain. "Did you make that hole in the foresail?" demanded the Old Man sternly.

"Er——" Paddy scratched his head perplexedly. "I suppose I did, sir. Fell through it, anyways."

"Well, you couldn't fall through it without making a hole in it, could you?"

Paddy, looking quite bewildered at the turn of the conversation, shuffled his feet, and replied "er—no, sir."

"Have you got a sea-bag?" demanded the Old Man.

"A say-bag?" Paddy looked more bewildered than ever.

"That's what I said," rapped out the captain.

"Sure, sir. I never come to say without one."

"Right. Well, cut the stiches of it and give it to Sails. He can patch that foresail with it."

Paddy did not answer. His jaw dropped and he gazed uncomprehendingly at the figure of the Old Man who had turned and was walking towards the after-end of the poop. Realizing that the interview was at an end, Paddy came towards us. Some of the men grinned at his discomfiture; others were sympathetic. "Well," he said, "I never heard the likes o' that since I came to say. Use me say-bag to patch a sail. An' me bag is forty years old if it's a day."

"How did dat tot of rum go down, Paddy?" asked Big Charlie with a twinkle.

Paddy gave a wry smile. "What drink I had, had plenty of salt in it."

"It's an imposition," and Kemp waved his arms to attract attention. "He's being imposed upon, that what he is. It's an insult to the lot of us." Nobody took any notice of him.

The matter of Paddy's bag was a subject for conversation and argument that evening in the dog-watches. To men whose homes were afloat and whose visits ashore but an occasional adventure, a new subject for discussion was always welcome. Had Paddy lost his life, that would have been just a demand made by the sea. But to have to give up his sea-bag. . .!

"It's his personal property the same as his shirt," said Turner.

"It's a sight more," remarked Hans. "A man don't 'ave de shirt all 'is life like he 'as de sea-bag."

Kemp, gesticulating as usual, shouted, "There's no capting what would take a sea-bag off *me*."

"That's cos you 'asn't got one," and the remark brought a laugh all round. Big Charlie ended the argument by saying, "What's de use of talkin'? If de Ol' Man says 'yous are dead'; well, yous are dead. Whatever we may say don't make no difference."

36

It so happened that Paddy never had to give up his sea-bag, nor did the Old Man ever make any further reference to it. Fritz, who was at the wheel at the time, said he saw a smile on the face of the captain when he turned his back on Paddy. It may have been just a legpull. It may have been to distract Paddy's mind from the fact that he had just escaped death by the thickness of a piece of canvas, by giving him a counter-shock!

On a Sunday morning I saw my first shark. The North-east Trades were failing us, and the light airs just enough to give the vessel steerage-way. I happened to be hanging out a shirt when suddenly I saw a dark three-cornered fin, about fifty yards away, moving slowly along the surface.

"Hi, Charlie!" I called, "that's a shark out there, isn't it?"

Charlie shielded his eyes against the sun. "Aye, that's a shark all right; looks a big one too. I'll go and ask the Old Man if we can catch him."

During all my time in sail I never knew a captain refuse permission to catch the first shark sighted on the passage, weather permitting, of course. The superstition was ingrained in the mind of every sailing-ship man that when the tail of a shark was nailed on to the jib-boom, fair winds would follow. It was only a matter of form that Charlie should ask his permission.

I was thrilled, and even the old-timers seemed excited at the prospect of catching this ancient enemy. Sails came along with a formidable-looking hook attached to about three feet of chain—"even a shark's teeth can't bite through chain," he explained to me. The fact that the steward actually issued a piece of meat for bait made me realize the importance of the occasion. Chips came aft with two capstan bars, and Big Charlie, I noticed, had an extra piece of rope in addition to the length secured to the end of the chain.

The watch had come aft by now, and we all invaded the sanctuary of the poop, from where the shark was to be caught, because the cut-away counter gave the men more facilities to carry out shark-catching routine. The bait was lowered down about an inch below the surface. Sharks have poor eyesight but are usually accompanied by a pilot-fish, which is about a foot long and of a bluish colour with dark transverse stripes. As the shark drew nearer, we could see the pilot-fish zigzagging to and fro over his head. Suddenly it darted towards the bait and, after examining it, returned to its lord and master. The shark altered course and swam lazily towards us. We could now see him distinctly, the black body about ten feet long, and his wicked, beady eyes in a sinister flattened head. When he was about four feet off the bait, he appeared to make a lunge at it, turning over as he did so, thus enabling us to see the terrible rows of teeth and white belly.

"Now!" roared Sails who had taken on the job of jerking the rope up at the right moment. We sprang to the rope and gave it a couple of heaves despite its tremendous jerking. Sails then held up his hand and the rope was made fast to a belaying-pin. I looked over the side. The shark's head was above the surface and he was thrashing the water into foam and spray in his efforts to free himself.

"Why don't we haul him up?" I asked Hans, who was next to me.

"'Cos he'd jump off de hook. We must secure him by de tail first before we lift him any higher."

Already Big Charlie had made a running noose, or bowline, around the rope holding the fish and had succeeded in shaking it over the shark's head. By skilful manœuvring he worked the noose towards the tail and then tautened it with a jerk.

"Right! Up together!" he bellowed, and the shark was lifted clear of the water. His body bent, curved and twisted convulsively in unavailing efforts to escape. Up he came to the level of the poop-rail then to be dragged inboard. Bump! He was on deck now and, for the moment, we had to scatter. At times he almost jumped clear of the deck, his tail whizzing around as high as our shoulders. The odds, however, were against him. The hook and tail ropes were secured to belaying-pins on the opposite sides of the poop, and Chips got in a hefty blow on his head with the capstan bar. Momentarily the shark relaxed and Hans took the opportunity of ramming the other capstan bar between the gaping jaws. At the same time three hands flung themselves on the tail end. A few more thuds from executioner Chips, and the shark was dead.

The carcass was then dragged off the poop on to the main deck. Paddy slit the belly open with his knife. "You never know," he said, a mischievous twinkle showing in his eye. "You might find a pair of sea-boots inside." I watched him rather apprehensively but, to my relief, there were no sea-boots. The tail was cut off and Chips, having removed the old tail which had been on the jib-boom since the last voyage, nailed the new on in its place.

Did the fair winds come? Alas, no. The *Denbigh Castle* was longer at sea on one passage than any other ship I know of.

Within a couple of days or so we had lost the North-east Trades altogether. Light baffling winds came from a dozen different directions within the course of a watch, and we spent most of our time hauling round the big yards trying to catch what gusts we could. Rain? Never had I imagined that rain could be so relentless or so solid. We paddled about, naked except for a pair of dungaree trousers, grousing and grumbling about the wet and the heat. When we were not pulling yards, we were catching rainwater in spreadout sails to replenish our water-tanks. On one particular morning I counted as many as a dozen waterspouts, each surmounted by an inverted cone-shape of black cloud, angry and sinister looking. One passed within a quarter of a mile of us and I noticed the Old Man looking at it rather anxiously. What would happen if a waterspout passed directly across the ship I did not know, but I imagined it would play havoc up aloft.

Kemp went round with the rest of us, rebuked into sullen silence; complaints are all part of life afloat, but the grouser must also be able to appreciate the lighter side. If not, he will eventually be told to "snap out of it!" or more likely become the butt of the other men's jokes. "You mustn't take any notice of Kemp," Paddy explained to the crew on one occasion during the rain. "This is the first time he's been properly clean, an' he doesn't like it." As Kemp's reluctance for washing was well known, the sally was not lost on Paddy's listeners, or on the victim.

The South-east Trades burst on the ship out of a rain squall followed by bright sunshine. Once again she resumed her purposeful course, and each night the Southern Cross climbed higher into the heavens.

Preparations were made for the fight which lay ahead. The fine-weather sails were sent down from aloft to be replaced by sturdy number one Cape Horn canvas. Life-lines, about five feet high, were rigged fore and aft along each side of the main deck and bowsed taut until they felt like steel bars. Weather-boards, about three feet high, were fitted just inside the fo'c'sle and half-deck doors into slots, finally to be made watertight by caulking them with oakum. These barricades had to be scrambled over by anybody wanting to go in or out. Extra tarpaulins were secured over the hatches, and sturdy planks lashed down on top of them to add further resistance to the on-slaughts of the mighty Cape Horn Greybeards. If a hatch were stove in, there could be little hope for either the ship or her crew.

On the foredeck, oilskins with broom-handles pushed through the sleeves and freshly coated with oil swung in the wind like a collection of yellow scarecrows. In the dog-watches, men could be seen giving repeated coats of dubbin or grease to their sea-boots.

South, and still farther south, and the weather gradually changed. The indigo-blue of the sea and sky lost its richness. The big stars receded. The sun no longer caressed us but shone with a cold glare on steel-grey waves capped with foam.

The day came when the wind suddenly shifted round to the south-west in a rain squall and there was a rush to trim the yards on to the other tack. Presently, from nowhere, an albatross appeared and hung over the mizzen truck for quite a while with motionless wings. Occasionally he moved his head from side to side to look at us, as though uncertain how to deal with our intrusion. At length, as though he had made up his mind, he dropped a "bomb" two feet from where the Old Man stood on the poop, and then swooped into a graceful glide.

Chips and Sails were put watch and watch with the rest of us. Up to the present, they had been off duty all night and only doing day work. For this reason (along with the cook and steward) they were called "idlers". As they worked from six in the morning for twelve hours, having only three-quarters of an hour off for breakfast and an hour for dinner, the title seemed rather ironical.

The Old Man, now dressed in sou'wester, a long oilskin coat and sea-boots, became a familiar figure standing under the lee of the poop dodger, or staggering for a few steps to and fro to try and take the stiffness out of his limbs. Hitherto he had lazed in a deck-chair with an open-necked shirt and a rather ancient-looking panama hat, well tanned by tropical suns. It was as though we had entered a different world, a world full of suspicion where dangers lurked seen and unseen, ready to trap the *Denbigh Castle*. Days would pass when she would be under six topsails, struggling over snowy ridges, then to descend with a swoop into the green valleys between. The resonant voice of the wind in the shrouds and maze of gear up aloft would rise and fall as the ship rolled towards or away from it. Sometimes the roar would remain crescendo as a black squall rushed from windward. Then the vessel would lie over obstinately and, with body stiffened, bore and crash her path through the seas. At such times came the blast of Mr. Owen's whistle which he wore attached to a lanyard around his neck, followed by the yell, "stand by topsail halliards!"

On December 10th, 1908, exactly sixty-one days after we had left Cardiff, we sighted the grim, black rocks known as Staten Island lying to the eastward of Cape Horn. The wind was strong to a gale, but from the northwards which, besides enabling ships to sail west, gives them smoother water. There was, however, a very high westerly swell. Was it, we wondered, the aftermath of a gale which had passed, or a forecast of the direction from which the wind would come?

The hands were jubilant. Would we have a straight run around the Horn? It was discussed in the cabin, the galley, the fo'c'sle and the half-deck. Charlie, with all the worldly weight of a second voyage apprentice, gave his opinion during the dinner-hour as we perched precariously on our sea-chests. "Last voyage," he said, "it was a fortnight before we got a slant. The whole trouble is that westerly winds are the prevailing winds, and when they come from another direction, they don't last long. Again, they say that the Pacific Ocean is a little bit higher than the Atlantic, and that means that there is a current against us as well."

42

It was our afternoon watch on deck, and the hands were employed making the inevitable rovings, a standing job during bad weather. Paddy happened to be working next to me and I asked him about our chances.

He jerked his thumb at our topsails. "The Ol' Man is missin' the chance. Now is the time to crack on every stitch she can carry, and what have we got? Six topsails! You can't monkey around when you're off Cape Stiff."

Suddenly we heard a blast from Mr. Owen's whistle followed by the call, "lay aft the boys". We dodged our way aft along the lee-side, splashing through the water, sometimes springing for the life-line or into the rigging whenever a dollop foamed on board. It had been impressed upon us that the weather-side was to be avoided at all costs unless duty took us there. With the ship lying over to leeward, leaving the high or windward side clear of water, it was a temptation to sprint along it when going forward or aft. There was always the danger, however, that a comber would unexpectedly roar over the rail and sweep the daring sailor down the hill to leeward.

Charlie, Gogan and I arrived on the poop, gasping and spluttering.

"Stand by your signal flags," ordered the Old Man.

We looked around and spotted a big four-masted barque roaring up astern. She actually had everything set except the royals. Mr. Owen had ensconced himself against a stanchion with his leg twined around it, watching the ship through the telescope. Presently, despite our heavy motion, he could read the name on her bow. "She's the *Kurt*, sir," he called out. "I think she belongs to Hamburg."

"That's right, I remember her well." Turning to us, he said, "hoist our ensign." We had it bent on all ready and hauled it up to the gaff.

Within fifteen minutes she was almost abeam, a magnificent

43

picture of beauty and strength. At one moment she would be rearing upwards and, as she overshot the head swell, we could see her forefoot, naked and streaming. The next instant she was careering down a watery slope to bury her nose into an oncoming mountain. At times her whole hull would disappear behind an intervening sea so that we could only see her from the lower topsails upwards. As she drew abeam, a flag signal suddenly fluttered up to her gaff.

"What has she got up, Mr. Owen?" demanded the Old Man impatiently. With the ship reeling over an arc of thirty degrees, I do not know how Mr. Owen kept the telescope trained on the flags at all. Presently he read them out, and the Old Man fussed over the signal-book. Suddenly he gave a bellow of rage, "The impertinence! Nothing but an insolent scoundrel!" and he closed the book with a bang.

"What did he say, sir?" asked Mr. Owen, rather injudiciously.

"Never mind what he said." He stumped off into the chart-room, taking the signal-book with him.

"Right," said the second mate. "That'll do the flags, boys."

The whole crew was now consumed with curiosity as to what signal the *Kurt* had made. It was no easy matter to keep a secret of this nature aboard a ship, and presently the news leaked out through the usual source, the galley. The steward, while serving a meal, had heard the Old Man complaining about the signal to "Old Jowl", the mate. He passed the tit-bit on to the cook who confided the matter in confidence to the sailmaker who could not resist relating it to the carpenter, and then it was but a matter of bush telegraph.

The captain of the *Kurt* had signalled, "Do you want a tow?" Our Old Man took it as being a sarcastic suggestion that, as he had only upper topsails set, he was too scared to set anything more and, in consequence, would have to be towed. Needless to say, the joke did not appeal to our Old Man's sense of humour, especially as subsequent events proved there was a grain of truth in it.

Shortly before midnight, during a heavy squall, the wind suddenly whipped about four points ahead, almost taking the ship aback. The kicking canvas, spilled by the wind, thundered above us. We could see the braces slackening and tautening convulsively due to the jerking of the yards. Were the braces to snap, anything could happen. Next instant the chain part of the main lower topsail parted and, whipping around like a live snake, gave off sparks every time it struck the steel yard.

Fortunately, Big Charlie was at the wheel (heaven help us had it been Kemp) and, without waiting for the order, put the wheel hard up. Fortunately, too, the vessel still had enough way upon her to respond to her helm and, by paying off, enabled the wind to fill her sails again.

Undoubtedly the *Denbigh Castle* had shipped a good crowd. The watch below, realizing that something serious was amiss, were tumbling out of their bunks. Most of them had lain down in their oilskins, even before "Old Jowl" had blown the long, penetrating blast on his whistle and yelled: "All hands on deck!"

The Old Man was on the poop now and gave Big Charlie a course to steer which brought the wind aft. With the fury of the elements behind her, the ship tore through the water like some frightened animal. In succession, big white-capped hills of water chased her, caught her and hurtled her forward in a welter of foam. The valleys between were so deep that sometimes the height of the following sea robbed the lower topsails of the tearing wind and the vessel slowed down momentarily. If, through this hesitation, her stern failed to rise in time and she "pooped", Big Charlie, steering-gear and wheel might all be hurled down somewhere on to the main deck. Should she "broach-to", through unskilled steering so as to bring the wind and sea on the beam, she could capsize or be dismasted.

Big Charlie steered with care.

The hail squall passed and a sickly moon rushed with dizzy speed through the storm-wracked clouds. We boys, being nearest, were on the poop first, and caught momentary glimpses of the men from both watches fighting their way through the swirling water on the main deck.

"Get that topsail secured first," said the Old Man to the mate. "Get that sheet bent on again and reset the sail."

Despite his game leg, this old fighter of the sea led us to the waist of the ship, encouraging and cursing us alternately. "Spread yourselves out, men; don't all of you get on to the bunt-lines. Clew-lines! How do you expect to get the sail up?" Nevertheless his eyes, which could see like a cat in the dark, were watchful of the sea and the ship. An extra lift of the stern, a higher lather of foam-capped water racing forward, shipping a hundred tons of water over the rail as it came, and a bellow would come from the depths of his lungs, "Hold on, everybody!"

Bunt-line and clew-lines were belayed in an instant, and we would hang on grimly with arms and legs to the nearest vantage point while the water above our waists tore viciously at our bodies. "Old Jowl", spitting out water and snorting like a walrus, would be at us again. "Hey, hey, what are you waiting for? Haul, men, haul!"

"Up aloft and stow!" Mr. Owen led the rush. In a sense it was a relief to get clear of the water. We dragged ourselves clear up the shrouds, pausing at times for the roll which would make the ascent less steep. Above us the mast waved helplessly in big semicircles.

The chain-sheet was more subdued now but still swinging

dangerously. It only wanted one twist in the wrong direction to knock several men off the yard. The sail was bulged out between the bunt-lines in a series of thrashing balloons, thumping and struggling in their efforts for release. It was noted and talked about by the men afterwards that Mr. Owen took up a position on the yard nearest to the dangerous sheet. That gained him a not forgotten respect for the rest of the voyage.

Presently the men were spread out right along the yard. "Now!" At the call from Mr. Owen, the men suddenly went berserk. With wild yells of defiance to the wind, they savagely attacked the sail. Gone was the rule, "one hand for the ship and one for yourself". Desperately they dug with both hands into the stiff canvas to make a crease and then, with a united heave, dragged it up to be held between their stomachs and the yard. Again the process was repeated, and yet again.

The sail was half-way in when the squall came. It hit the ship brutally like a blow from a sledge-hammer. It tore at the sail and the men in a frenzy of invisible strength, and the jagged hailstones, travelling like bullets, drew blood. The men silently concentrated their determination and strength on holding on to the sail. If one of them loosened his hold, even for an instant, the whole sail might slip again.

The squall passed. An apology for a moon darted out from behind the blackness and dived into another cloud. The wind eased as though exhausted. "Now, boys, now!" A yell came from every throat, but this time without defiance. It was a triumphant cry, a cry of victory as the sail was finally rolled up on to the yard and safely secured with its gaskets.

A depressing greyness in the atmosphere, telling us that the sun must have risen, found all hands still on deck. The three upper topsails had been taken in, and the refractory sheet repaired and bent on. Throughout the night the ship had been

47

travelling southwards towards the sixtieth latitude—the domain of the icebergs. Captain Evans had considered it inadvisable to heave-to in the dark. To bring her round to the wind when, at one period of the turn she would be broadside on to such a high sea, would be hazardous, yet the ship could not sail south, indefinitely.

Shortly after the arrival of a so-called dawn, the order was passed to brace the yards up on the starboard tack. The men hauled on the braces like automatons. They had reached the limits of normal physical endurance, but still kept on. We could see more clearly now in the growing light, and looked at one another with strange curiosity. Our eyes were red and bleary and our faces encrusted with salt, with water dripping from limp beards and moustaches. Mis-shapenly dressed in heavy sea-boots, and oilskins lashed at the ankles, wrists and around our waists, we must have looked like beings from another world.

"All hands on the poop!" The bellow from "Old Jowl" told us that the Old Man had made up his mind. He stood with legs outstretched beside Big Charlie, who by now had been at the wheel for seven hours. His eyes kept glancing to windward at the sky and the sea. Three seas, bigger than their fellows, passed under us and then the order came: "Down helm!"

Twisting and rolling as though in pain, the *Denbigh Castle* started on her semicircle. As she came into the trough, a wall of green water capped with snow sped towards her out of the murk. We held our breath. Gallantly she rose to it, flung herself over forty-five degrees, hung there a few seconds and then straightened up. The next sea caught her nearer the bow, and she soared upwards as though about to leave the water altogether. The main danger, however, was now passed. Coming close to the wind she lost headway, and presently lay hove-to, quite prepared to ride out whatever Cape Horn might send her.

Up aloft and stow!

Members of the crew. The Author (holding monkey) and extreme left (sitting) fellow-apprentice, Gogan Lawlor, also on his first voyage

"That'll do, the watch." During my life-time I've never heard more welcome words. What matter that our half-deck had a foot of water swilling from side to side to slap the bunk-boards of the lower bunks? That our bed-clothes were soaking? Waiting no longer than to take off our sou'westers, we climbed into our bunks and slept.

CHAPTER FIVE

CHRISTMAS DUFF

THE day, Christmas, 1908. The view, Staten Island, which
we had first sighted on our arrival off the Horn over a fortnight ago. The weather, according to "Old Jowl's" log-book I
had peeped at in the chart-room, "gale, force six to seven, high
sea, vessel hove-to under lower topsails and fore topmast
stay-sail." Not exactly the ingredients for a Happy
Christmas.

It was my misfortune to be the Peggy that day, and my first
job was to bail the water out of the half-deck. Truly a thankless
job, since whenever a sea tumbled aboard, the water squirted
through the jamb of the door. The bailing-out process had to be
carried out about every two hours. As it was Christmas Day, we
were spared the wearisome chore of making rovings under the
fo'c'sle head. Being hove-to, the ship needed little attention.
Even the man at the wheel had practically nothing to do, as the
helm remained half-way down to keep the vessel close to the
wind and sea. Charlie, Gogan and I just lay on the tops of our
bunks dressed in oilskins, in case there should be an emergency
call.

"Hey, Peggy! Half-past eleven. What about the dinner?"
My reverie was broken by Charlie. I threw my legs over the
bunk and slid down on to my sea-chest. This was a momentous
occasion, and we had been looking forward to it since the day
began. The great event of course was Christmas duff, consisting
of flour, raisins and molasses. We had no false hopes as to its

50

flavour. To us it was something additional to eat, something to help satisfy that nagging hunger.

The cook, aged about sixty, was gaunt and wore a straggly grey beard invariably stained with tobacco juice. His galley was frequented by myriads of cockroaches which scuttled over the bulk-heads and deck-head with the activity of ants. Whether he deliberately put a few into the soup or they just fell in, we never could decide but they were usually there. Rumour had it that he had been a teacher of singing before drink had driven him to sea. The legend that he was a cook had long since died.

He had quite a good repertoire of Welsh hymns which he sang in a cracked voice, occasionally, when he was not volubly cursing the ship, the weather or somebody who had annoyed him. He had a rough-and-ready method of dealing with com-plainants. He would seize his chopper and, with an insane glare in his eyes, rush upon the offender. Whether he would have used the chopper, nobody knew, and nobody waited to see. Nevertheless he was kind to us boys when we did not tease him, and sometimes even gave us crusts of stale bread.

Fetching the dinner required a certain preparation, judgment and skill. On this important occasion the weather demanded that I should follow the routine faithfully. I stood tensely in-side the door with my hand on the handle, listening for a lull, and waiting for that "feel" of the ship which tells you that she is going to relax from her rolling for ten seconds or so to take a "breather". You can tell also, by a premature jerk to wind-ward, that a sea is likely to sweep on board. It is no use then trying to get to the galley as the decks would be full up.

After three very heavy rolls, the exhausted ship steadied herself. Now was my chance. I threw open the door, clambered over the barricade, no easy job in stiff oilskins and heavy sea-boots, jumped down into the water and slammed the door.

Nipping round the corner I sped, if one can call it speeding, along a deck sloping like a house roof, and reached the galley in safety.

Cookie apparently had been bailing too, for there was only a few inches or so of water swilling around his feet. His stove was fitted over the top with iron bars, running from front to back, which he could drop into sockets, thus preventing his cooking utensils from being thrown on to the floor.

"Ah, Paddy, it is you," and he handed me a big oval hanging-pot fitted with a lid. "Here's the soup. You want to be careful, look you."

"You bet, Cookie," I answered. "I'll be back in five minutes for the rest."

"And you bring the pot back with you, see. It is best for you to carry the dinner that way," he called out after me in his sing-song voice as I disappeared through the door. My passage back passed without incident. Gogan was peeping through the partly-open door and, having handed him the pot, I clambered into the half-deck. We poured the soup into our enamel mugs, and the first course was finished. On my next journey, the cook presented me with salted pork, also an extra ration of bread, a pleasant surprise indeed as the potatoes on board were long since exhausted.

I cannot say that I thoroughly enjoyed my dinner. It was not just because the pork was tainted, for our sense of taste had become well-blunted by now. What weighed upon my mind was the importance of my mission, the fear that something might go wrong when I was fetching the duff. With almost a sense of premonition, I took extra precautions, I tied a lanyard around my neck and secured the end to the handle of the pot in which the duff would be carried. Thus, should it be torn from my hand by a sea, at least it would not go overboard unless, of course, I went that way, too.

"You should not have that lanyard, look you," said Cookie when I appeared in the galley.

"Why not?" I demanded. "I think it's a jolly good idea."

"It is the only saucepan that I have." He turned towards his stove to shift a kettle on the fire. "If you go overboard, I will lose it, see?" An angry impulse arose within me to tell him exactly what I thought of him and his pot, only at that moment he turned around to show the twinkle in his eyes. I grinned. "Away you go now, bach, and take great care of that saucepan, mind you."

"You bet," I answered and, as the opportunity seemed favourable, stepped out of the galley door to make my return journey. I had gone about twenty paces when I realized that, in my anxiety to return quickly with the duff, I had started my journey too soon. That significant jerk to windward was ominous. It meant that the valley between the two seas was steeper and narrower than usual, and that she would be presenting her deck to the next wave before she had time to roll back. Consequently the sea would come aboard. I had possibly five seconds in which to make up my mind. Return to the galley? Impossible. I would never make it. Jump for the rigging? No. I might be just on top of the rail when I would be caught, and in a favourable position to be carried overboard. The life-line stretching along the deck? Realizing that it was my only refuge, I sprang. With the pot hanging by its lanyard around my neck, I hung back downwards, my legs and feet interlocked, and both hands clutching the line tightly to my chest. It came. It towered above the low-lying rail and struck the ship along half of her length to rear itself up exultingly. The upper half of the snow-capped green wall hesitated, tottered, and then came tumbling down to tear madly in a devastating rush across the ship, obliterating from sight everything in its path. A wild glance, and then I took a deep breath and shut my eyes and mouth. Next instant it had engulfed me, solid, frenzied water, terrifying in its intensity.

In that instance my whole world was narrowed down to a three-inch rope. Upon it, and the strength of my arms and legs depended my very existence. Suddenly I felt afraid. It seemed as though giant fingers were slowly yet firmly lifting me off my place of refuge. The strain seemed too much for my arm-sockets. My breath was going too, partly because I dare not open my mouth, and partly because the lanyard holding the pot was pulling at my neck like a hangman's rope.

As my fingers were being dragged from their hold, I saw light showing through my closed eyelids and, simultaneously, the terrific drag stopped. I looked around. The decks were full as high as the rails. The ship lay quiet, as though in protest against the weight of several extra hundred tons. I lowered myself and the water came up to my waist. As I ploughed my way aft, helping myself along with the iron hand-rail outside the half-deck, I looked up and saw Mr. Owen grinning at me from the poop. "Brute," I muttered, retrieving the pot floating beside me. "Pity he can't find something else to laugh at."

As a matter of fact, Mr. Owen's grin was one of relief. He told me afterwards that he had lost sight of me for at least fifteen seconds and actually glanced out-board to see if I had gone over the side. "First, the pot showed up like a marking-buoy," he said, "and a few seconds later, I saw your head. It should be a lesson to you to be more careful," he admonished. I thought it a stupid remark. Did he think I had undergone such an ordeal for fun? Still, what could one expect from officers any-way?

I reached the half-deck door and climbed inside. "Hello," said Charlie, "where you been? Thought you were never coming along with that duff."

"'Never' is right," I answered petulantly, still feeling a bit shaken, and then told them about it.

"More fool you," remarked Gogan with his mouth full. "You should have watched your chance." I made no reply. A ship's half-deck is no place to look for sympathy.

The *Denbigh Castle* was still battling off Cape Horn in March. Two months of gales, hopes, and disappointments, had dragged on. For a week or so we might lose sight of Staten Island, but it always reappeared with monotonous regularity.

To add to our miseries, the full ration of sugar, butter and flour had become exhausted. The men, rightly claiming that the Owners had defaulted in the agreement made in the Articles, refused to do any work outside the necessary handling of the ship. The decks were never scrubbed and gradually became covered with green slime. The crew now went about their duties, sullen and disheartened. No longer did one hear their cheery "aha-yah" when they pulled on the braces, or a shanty when hoisting a yard. Men cannot sing when their oil-skins are worn and leaking, their sea-boots filling with water every time they go on deck, and wrists chafed into sores or with boils on their bottoms. Further, they were now hungry.

"Say, Paddy," I asked my old Cork friend one day as he was showing me how to make an intricate fancy knot, "do you think we will ever get round the Horn?"

He squirted a well-chewed tobocco quid on to the deck. "No, she'll never get round while this Old Man is in charge. He's lost his nerve. I told you two months ago that you must take chances off the Horn when the wind is fair. Remember the *Kurt*? Remember her flying past us under upper-t'gallant sails an' us only with topsails?"

"Aye, that's the time the Old Man lost his rag over her signal."

"The very same. Well, she's probably discharged by now an' lying pretty in the sun loadin' another cargo. That man knew the Horn, an' what's more, he knew how to sail his ship. Our Ol' Man will have to do something soon 'cos the weather will be gettin' bad any time now."

"Getting bad?" I queried, wondering if he was pulling my leg.

"Sure," and he cut a fresh quid off his plug. "The gales will come more frequent, and the cold; well, everything gets froze up aloft, running-gear, sails an' the like. I've seen the hands pouring boiling water on the brace-blocks to try and get them to work. Besides, we're short of provisions and we 'aint got no clothes."

"What can the Old Man do, then?"

"Well, he could take us to Port Stanley in the Falkland Islands an' refit us an' then come back an' have another dart at the Horn. But we'd be slap into winter by then."

"I never want to be around here again once we leave it," I remarked, dismayed.

"Alternative like, we could turn about, make a fair wind of it by running the eastern down. We wouldn't be the first ship to do that. We'd have to call into a South African or an Australian port, of course."

"Anything would be better than this," I said bitterly. Apart from the hardships, I was very worried about my people. What an anxiety they must be undergoing with month after month passing and still no news of the *Denbigh Castle*. Possibly the *Kurt* had reported us on her arrival at a Chilean port, but that would have increased rather than relieved their anxiety. *Denbigh Castle* sighted off Cape Horn over two months ago, but still no news of her!

To abandon the battle of Cape Horn and choose the alternative route, that of making a passage right around the world, is

56

no easy decision for a sailing-ship master. Not only does it lengthen the voyage by five months or so, but there is no hope of the vessel earning any money for her owners, and the quickest way a master can earn the disfavour of his firm is to run their ship at a loss. No wonder, therefore, that Captain Evans hesitated.

On the morning of March 9th, the decision was made for him. As the sun struggled up above the horizon, the red turned to crimson, and the foam-capped waves looked as though tinged with blood. It suddenly became very cold. "De winter is not far off," remarked Big Charlie to the cook, as he paused at the galley door after his trick at the wheel. From the poop, the Old Man eyed the sea and sky with misgivings and then went into the chart-room to look at the barometer. The manner of its falling might almost be compared to the movement made by the minute-hand of a clock. Despite the vicious knocks he gave it with his knuckles, it still continued to fall, although at the time there was only a moderate breeze blowing.

Returning to the poop, he sniffed the air to windward. "We'll get that lower mizzen-topsail off her, Mr. Owen," he said. "There's some dirt knocking around."

The men came down from aloft, leaving the mizzen, now devoid of sail, naked and useless. They went forward blowing on their blue fingers or flapping their arms.

"It's always 'take in sail, take in sail'," complained Kemp, "an' 'ardly ever settin' it. What kind of a capting 'ave we at all? He'll never get us nowhere." Most of the men gave grunts of assent. For once, they felt in agreement with Kemp.

The wind came without warning. It came like an avenging terror, an invisible force of appalling velocity out of a void where no cloud betrayed its coming. It whipped the surface off the tormented sea and hurtled it in dense masses of spume horizontally through the streaming atmosphere. It sounded as though the lid of hell had been lifted to release a million demons, some of whom sobbed and moaned in chorus while the rest maintained an agonizing shriek in crescendo. The ship being under but two lower topsails, gallantly withstood the sudden onslaught. She lay over slowly, reluctantly.

Captain Evans, with body bent, and his long oilskin coat flapping around his legs, forced himself along the poop under the lee of the dodger where "Old Jowl" was standing. "Call all hands," he bellowed into his ear. "We don't know what's behind all this!"

Figures in yellow oilskins could be seen struggling aft, the rims of their sou'westers at various unorthodox angles as the wind snatched at their hats. Their oilskins were lashed at the wrists, ankles and waists in case their three-pound-a-month calling should suddenly demand that they be up to their necks in water. Hardened seamen as they were, they knew that this was no ordinary wind. They moved from one vantage point to another as the movements of the ship dictated, always watchful, always wary for the unexpected. They mustered on the poop, seeking out sheltered corners in the lee of the chart-house and cabin skylights. Mr. Owen had now joined the captain and "Old Jowl" under the weather-dodger. Except for an occasional glance to windward, their eyes kept turning to the two straining topsails. Hans, the Norwegian, stood stolidly at the wheel, his face impassive except for the rhythmic movement of his jaws chewing tobacco.

The sea which at first seemed to have been almost flattened by the initial onslaught of the wind, now started to rise. Cape Horn grey-beards, magnificent in their splendour, from whose curling crests the wind whipped spindrift higher than the main-yard, moved relentlessly forward in procession, tossing the ship to dizzy heights and angles, and then roaring away to leeward.

I found myself next to Paddy, hanging on to the hand-rail on the lee-side of the chart-house. He put his mouth to my ear. "Nature is fed up with this 'ere ship being so long off the Horn," he said. "She seems to be musterin' her forces proper this time an' no mistake."

I made no reply. Conversation was difficult, and I was cold and hungry. "'Ere," and Paddy bumped me to attract my attention, "put this in your jaw," I looked down and saw that he was handing me a quid of tobacco. Much as I wanted to appear and act like a sailor, I shuddered at the thought of chewing. However, as the tobacco ration had been cut a couple of weeks ago, I appreciated his kindly thought.

"Thanks, Paddy, but I could never chew that stuff. I think it would make me sick."

"It won't if you don't swally it," he answered. "You needn't chew it if you don't want to, but it'll warm you up," and he pressed the cutting off his plug into my hand. Rather than offend, I reluctantly slipped the quid into my cheek and was agreeably surprised to feel a warm glow coming to my face. I nodded to him appreciatively and he grinned his delight.

Mr. Owen saw the wave first. His warning yell, "Hold on, everybody!" whisked down to us and, startled we gazed out to windward. Instinctively we knew that no wind, not even the tearing fury we were now experiencing, could be responsible for such a stupendous hill of water and foam. Three or four waves still intervened between this gargantuan sea and the ship, and we watched as though mesmerized. Possibly it had originated through some marine disturbance thousands of miles away, and had grown to its immensity during its unhindered journey around the base of the world. Maybe a 'berg had turned over. Who could tell? What did it matter? It was almost upon us.

Nobody could ever say that the *Denbigh Castle* did not do her best. Nobly she soared upwards, her decks canting to a steeper

angle the higher she climbed. Approaching the summit, however, there was no slope for her to climb, only a perpendicular
wall, a green swiftly-moving cliff which intervened between her
and the valley on the other side. Then the cliff hit her.

The ship gave a toppling lurch, and the mighty cataract of
water passed completely over her in a confused turmoil of leaping foam. The lofty masts suddenly swept over to such an acute
angle that the main-yard touched the now departing sea. Then
came a strange sensation as though the hull was dropping into a
void, and only the violent thud told us that the vessel was still
waterborne.

The *Denbigh Castle*, although on the other side of the hill,
did not roll back.

From my position, clinging grimly to the chart-house rail, I
was able to look for'ard. So far as the hull was concerned, I
could only see the fo'c'sle head, the tops of the deck-houses and
the upper rail of the weather-bulwarks. Everywhere else was
leaping, churning water. On the poop, several of the hands had
been washed or thrown down to leeward, to be saved from
sliding overboard by the wash-board, and were struggling to their
feet or reaching out to grasp the hands of those above them so as
to be pulled up the slope. Glancing to windward, I saw the
captain and the two mates, the water streaming off them, still
clinging to the weather-rail.

Their protecting canvas-dodger was gone. Gone, too, the
wooden wheel-box which shielded the steering-gear, but Hans
still stood at the wheel clutching the spokes. His face had the
same stolid expression, and I believe he was actually chewing.
The ship appeared to lie still, with water rushing over her, not
unlike a half-tide rock. At times she made feeble efforts to right
herself, like some wounded animal trying to rise to its feet, but
she would sink back again as though the effort gave her too much
pain.

"Old Jowl", despite his gammy leg, performed some acrobatic feats with the aid of the tail-end of a bunt-line and came down the sloping deck amongst the men. "Are you all here?" he shouted. "Is any of you missing?" We looked around vacantly at one another. Beyond recognizing the familiar faces of those present, we seemed incapable of realizing whether or not anybody were absent. Mr. Owen solved the problem He counted us twice. "Jowl!" he suddenly exclaimed. "Where's Kemp?"

Kemp? Again the men looked at one another with blank faces, as though expecting one of them to produce the missing man out of his pocket.

"If I know anything of Kemp he's taken good care not to be drowned," said "Old Jowl". "Here, open that chart-room door, somebody." Matthews, hanging on to the chart-house rail with one hand, turned the handle and eased open the door with the other. The mate clambered over the high doorstep. Suddenly there was a commotion from inside. "Old Jowl's" angry bellow mingled with a high-pitched appeal. "Oh! Oh! Don't! You've no right. . . . You . . ." Next instant Kemp appeared, looking very frightened and with his left eye blackening visibly. He stumbled out on to the poop and would have slid down the careening deck had somebody not caught him. The hands glared at him aggressively.

Kemp eyed them fearfully, then, with that strange mixture of courage and bluff he so often called upon when cornered, cried, "I didn' do no 'arm! I am a man just the same as an off'cer is. If you fools like to stand out in the . . ."

"Shut up," said Big Charlie, "or I vill thrown you overboard mineself." Then somebody laughed. Apparently, when all hands had been called aft, Kemp had noticed that not only were the captain and the two mates on the poop, but also the steward, and that the chart-house would be empty until a further order was passed. With his native astuteness he had unobtrusively stepped into the chart-house and closed the door behind him.

The *Denbigh Castle* had freed herself of a considerable amount of water. Owing to her list to leeward she presented an abnormally high side to the oncoming seas which came aboard less frequently. Two hours passed, and she was still afloat.

Suddenly Paddy gave me a nudge with his elbow. "The wind is droppin'," he said. "Have you noticed it?"

"What does it matter whether it drops or not," I answered listlessly. "We couldn't get anywhere before this happened, so what chance have we now?"

"Plenty," and Paddy paused to shoot a chewed quid from his lips. "The old girl is not going to throw her hand in now. The trouble is our cargo has shifted an' that's why she has this list. The hatches have held and I'll bet she's makin' no water. If the Old Man gets a chance to wear ship, it'll make a great difference to her, you'll see."

Wear ship? Why had the idea not struck me before? By setting sail on the jib-boom, her bow would fall away and gradually the wind would come behind her so that she would steer. By continuing round in a big circle, the weather would come on the low side, then, if sail were set, the wind would help to straighten her up. My despair gave way to hope. "Paddy," I exclaimed, "you should have been a captain instead of just an A.B. in the fo'c'sle."

My remark seemed to tickle him. "Me, a captain," he replied chuckling. "I could handle a ship all right, but what about me navigating? I don't know nothing about figures, an' what's more," he put his mouth confidentially to my ear, "I don't even know how to write me name."

"Look!" The exclamation came from Fritz. From the galley funnel, canted at a crazy angle, we saw smoke.

"Hey, Cookie, your galley, it vos gone on fire!" Stiff jaws released themselves in a grin at the crack. The men glanced around, awaiting a caustic reply from the cook who was never short of an answer. He was nowhere to be seen.

Voices which had long remained silent, could now be heard exclaiming, "Where's the cook. . . .? Slipped overboard . . . not on your life . . . old blighter must have gone to the galley . . . 'e wouldn't have the guts . . . the stove is alight. . . ." Possibly the mystery as to how the ship kept afloat was almost equalled by how the cook lighted a fire. His mode of entry was not so difficult as at first imagined. There was a fore-and-aft bridge running from the level of the poop to the top of the half-deck. Having reached the half-deck he was able to clamber along its top to the galley skylight which, incidentally, was boarded up and further protected by a canvas cover. Removing these, he had lowered himself down. The water must have been swilling around up to his knees; indeed it must have been very close to the fireplace, but Cookie still made coffee.

We saw his head eventually emerging from the skylight, his straggly grey hair and beard whisking in the wind, the skinny arms in the shirt-sleeves rolled up as he hoisted himself upon the edge. An enamelled mug hung from his neck, and around his waist he had secured a rope upon which he started to haul. On the end was a saucepan, the one which had contained my famous duff. We gazed at him in amazement, none of us attempting to move. Putting the saucepan beside him, he turned towards the poop and made a funnel with his hands. Much of what he said was lost, but we heard, "standing there like a crowd of . . . sheep; why the . . . don't some of you come an' give a . . . hand . . . coffee!"

A croaked cheer broke out. Coffee! At the prospect of a hot drink, the possibility was forgotten that we might all be thrown into the sea. "Coffee! The old blighter has made some coffee!"

Forgotten the days of the half-cooked meat and cockroach soup; now he was not only the most wonderful cook that ever trod a deck, but a blinkin' hero.

The coffee was without milk or sugar. It had coffee-grains floating thickly on the surface; no doubt it also contained a few cockroaches and tasted strongly of salt water, but it was hot. Never before or since have I appreciated a cup of coffee more.

CHAPTER SIX

THE WHITE FEATHERS

"WEAR ship!" It was the Old Man who suddenly snapped out the order. From a lifelong habit, some of the men repeated the words mechanically, but nobody moved. "Wear ship?" echoed somebody. "Wear a ship that's lyin' on her side like a stove-in biscuit-tin?"

"Wear ship! Do you hear?" shouted the mate as he clambered down the life-line that had been rigged thwart-ships across the poop and advanced towards the men. "Come along, get moving. . . . Are you sailors or just a beauty chorus? Six of you go for'ard an' get the inner and outer jibs on her. Here you, Turner, Mathews, Fritz, and you, what's your name, make a break for it." Stiffly the men released themselves from the various positions in which they had settled. How could they wear ship with the lee-side so full of water that it even covered the pins where the braces, so essential for swinging the yards, were belayed? "Old Jowl", with flaming red-rimmed eyes and bristling walrus moustache, advanced on them threateningly.

"Come on, lads!" Mr. Owen stood at the top of the weather poop-ladder and was beckoning to them. As quick as their stiff limbs would allow, they followed him down the poop-ladder on to the main deck.

Although all the water lay on the lee-side, leaving the weather-side clear, heavy seas occasionally toppled over the rail and roared down to leeward in a smother of jumping foam. The deck sloped too much for the men to adopt the usual dodge-and-run tactics. It was a case of making a dive from one

E   65

belaying-pin to another or clinging to the braces where they ran inside the rail; a constant readiness for that preliminary thud outside the hull foretelling that a sea would rear itself above the rail and obliterate them. One by one, gasping, spitting, shaking their heads as a swimmer does when he surfaces, they arrived on the raised portion of the fo'c'sle head.

It seemed lonely there in that three-cornered, wind-swept platform isolated by heavy seas from the poop where their shipmates stood. Although heavy water failed to reach it, it was under a continuous bombardment of flying spray. At the apex, the long jib-boom, sometimes lifting skywards, sometimes dipping perilously close to the passing sea beneath, looked gaunt and bare. It was Turner and Fritz who clambered out, not unlike two birds clinging to a swaying branch of a tree, and loosed the inner and outer jibs. The others, clinging to the anchors and windlass capstan, prepared as best they could to haul away on the halliards as soon as Turner and Fritz returned to the comparative safety of the fo'c'sle head.

Nobody, least of all themselves, could tell how these head sails, so essential to enable the ship to pay off, or push her bow away from the wind, were set. Nevertheless, bellying and straining, they were sheeted home, and the toilers once again made their journey along the main deck to regain the so-called sanctuary of the poop.

"Stand by to haul on weather main-braces!" The crucial moment was now at hand, and the Old Man balanced himself on the weather-side of the chart-house, grimly watching ship and sea.

Could the ship, when in such a crippled condition, be manœuvred at all? And if she did, how would she behave when, during her turning, the wind and sea came beam on?

Captain Evans had been watching. "Now!" he yelled, "square the main-yard! Jump to it, men, there's a chance now!"

66

Mr. Owen slithered down the lee ladder and found himself waist deep in water. With surprising speed, "Old Jowl" followed him, his gammy leg not allowing him to take more than one step at a time. One could almost imagine, as they forced their way to the main-braces, that they were actually in the sea, for the bulwarks beside them were out of sight at times.

Opposite to them on the high side, the hands had now collected, clinging to what supports they could as they waited for the mates to slack away the braces. The pins, however, to which they were secured, had first to be found, and the water now reached almost to the armpits of "Old Jowl" and Mr. Owen. When they bent down to grope for the pins, the water came up to their necks. Suddenly "Old Jowl" stood upright like a walrus surfacing. "Haul away!" Not only his bellow but his determination against such odds inspired the men. Slipping, sliding, swinging and hauling on a deck sloping like the roof of a house, they stuck grimly to their task. The yard came round in little jerks, sometimes wanting to swing back again. "Hold and haul, lads," was the cry. So they held and hauled until the flap on the weather leech of the topsail told them that the wind had been spilled out of it. Once again the apparently impossible had been accomplished.

"Lay aft, everybody!" Nobody wasted any time in obeying the Old Man's call. They knew that, as soon as the ship paid off, those devilish seas would come up from abeam and take charge of the main deck. They knew, too, that they might roll the ship over altogether. As Paddy remarked to me afterwards, "if she capsized, it wouldn't matter where you stood, but it would be more respectable-like to be drownded from the poop."

"Up helm! An extra man to the wheel!" Zero hour had arrived. The Old Man had jammed himself against the compass binnacle. Possibly he was wondering if the order he had now given would be his last. The two mates, doubtless from habit alone, remained up to windward. The men, from traditional custom, left them a clear space. The inactivity seemed to be a tragedy in itself. Hope lay in the coming of the wind and sea on the quarter, but the dangerous part of the turn, when wind and sea would be abeam, must be completed first. At the moment she might have been without a crew for all that could be done. Their fate lay with God, the ship, and the sea. Nobody spoke. It were as though our thoughts were too deeply concentrated on willing the vessel to do what was asked of her. Her bows rose wearily, almost in distaste, then to slither down into the succeeding valley. If only a temporary lull would come to give her a chance! Instead, a big sea tore brutally across the deck.

Suddenly an irregular lump of water struck her squarely on the side of the fo'c'sle head. It seemed to rouse her, her bows swung slowly to leeward. Laboriously the bows continued to lift and dip, but with each rise they swung in the right direction. The wind came abeam. An angry wall of foaming water rushed at her but she canted herself in time and, thwarted, the sea passed under her. The wind was getting behind the main lower topsail now, and it bellied out eagerly.

Big Charlie was the first to break the long silence. "She's moving!" The men suddenly burst into exclamations. A dozen of them echoed Charlie's cry. A ship moving, however slowly, was a ship that could be steered, and a ship that could be steered could be controlled.

The wind was almost aft now and the vessel dragged herself through the water like some wounded animal trying to make its escape. A threatening big sea would hoist her stern upwards, and she would be carried along on its slope. Then, as the sea sped forward to cock her bows up, she would stop as though spent with the effort. Running before the wind has proved to be a dangerous procedure with some ships, due perhaps to the fact that they had not enough sail set and did not get away from the following sea quick enough, or that their counters, through being too fine, had not enough area for the water to lift them sufficiently. In either case a ship may "poop" and the sea, sweeping from stern to bow, carries all before it. Mr. Owen told us boys that such a disaster had befallen "Old Jowl" when he was but a young man, and that he had been fortunate to escape with only a broken leg. Apparently he was at the wheel at the time and was eventually found half drowned somewhere near the foremast, still clutching the wheel!

Possibly Captain Evans may have had the story of "Old Jowl's" experience in mind when he ordered the upper topsails to be set. Again, no doubt, he realized that when he brought the low side of the ship towards the wind, the extra pressure aloft would give her a better chance to straighten up. Cold and stiff, alternatively sweating under the efforts of superhuman exertions, the hands shambled around to the goading of "Old Jowl's" orders.

Hearing somebody pass remarks about "task-masters", he summed up the situation sharply. "It's work or die, my man, and as I don't want to die, you've got to work." Suddenly his temper got the better of him. Whipping round on the offender with upraised fist he roared, "Get up aloft and loose that topsail, you . . ." He was never short of words. It was not until the man was well up the shrouds that the mate, realizing that he must be out of earshot, ceased to curse.

As the day advanced, the squalls became less frequent, and the pale sun threw out oblique rays which at least gave us sunshine, if no heat. We found ourselves again on the poop, that dais from whose vantage-point we had watched the unfolding drama of a ship fighting for her life, and ours. The final scene was now about to be enacted, and one which would decide the fate of us all. Everything was now ready. The yards had been trimmed on the other tack, and all that remained was to alter course so that the wind and sea came on the side to which she listed. "Starboard three points!" We sensed the suppressed excitement in the voice of the Old Man, and a nervous, electric tension passed through the crowd. We could feel the wind creeping around on to the port quarter. We held our breath as a vicious dollop of water slithered up the sloping deck, curled, and fell like a surf-roller on a beach. Another sea came roaring up under the port quarter, and then—it happened.

As though in anger at the prolonged restraint, the *Denbigh Castle* wrenched her lee-side out of the water. The jerk was so great that she rolled in the opposite direction. Volumes of water lying on the low side, tore in cataracts across the deck which increased her roll. The wash-ports shot open and water sluiced over the side. With wash-ports and scupper-holes discharging tons of water off the decks into the sea, one could feel buoyancy and life being coaxed back into the ship. For the second time that day the men gave vent to a hoarse cheer. Their eyes, red-rimmed with salt, which had previously shown weariness, if not despair, now glistened with hope renewed.

Mr. Owen looked across at us and then at the ship, smiling appreciatively. It was difficult to judge the sensations of "Old Jowl". Since his face was so obscured by the heavy moustache and bushy eyebrows, nobody could read correctly what lay beneath the undergrowth. Occasionally a twinkle showed in his eyes, and when he rowed me up over something or other, I used to glance at his eyes to see if he were really annoyed or not. On this occasion he showed his pleasure by not quelling immediately the pathetic laughter and chatter of the men upon that sacred of all precincts, the poop. Possibly Captain Evans, although he had performed less physical labour than any of us, looked the most tired. His haggard face was deeply lined and, for all his change in expression, he seemed to be insensible to the recent recovery of the *Denbigh Castle*. Looking back now,

I am confident that he would freely have exchanged places with any of his comparatively carefree apprentices. Apart from his failure off Cape Horn and the acute anxiety about his ship and her crew, he faced a lack of sympathy, if not a severe reprimand from his Owners because no profits could result from the voyage.

He turned to Hans, who was still at the wheel. "Steer north-east."

Paddy plucked at my sleeve. "Say, did you hear that? Course north-east."

"Well . . ." I began, and then the significance penetrated. "You don't mean . . . ?"

Paddy nodded. "Yes, it looks like good-bye to Cape Horn, for the present at any rate. The Old Man's packing up on it, an' I don't blame him. The ship's not fit to stand up to it any longer, nor the crew if it comes to that. Just look at her now."

I looked. She rolled heavily to port, although it was the weather-side against wind and sea, and when she rolled the other way, her masts went little beyond an upright position. Were she to be put on the other tack, more than likely she would become unmanageable again.

"It's what I told you, cargo's shifted," and Paddy nodded his head sagely. "It's stickin' out a mile." Paddy was right. Captain Evans was left with no alternative but to run the eastern down.

"That'll do the watch. Relieve the wheel." The stentorian voice of "Old Jowl" restored us to sanity. That not only meant that the watch due to be off duty could go below but, in the opinion of the captain and his officers, any immediate danger was now passed and the normal routine of life aboard ship could be resumed. The men looked at one another. "Blest if I know whether I'm watch on deck or below," said somebody.

He could hardly be blamed. All hands had been on deck for ten hours.

There are occasions when the life of a sailor is like that of a cat which, when chased by a dog, jumps on to a wall and starts to wash itself, forgetting apparently that but a few seconds ago it had escaped violent death. Playing tip-and-run with a watery grave for most of the day had been enough but the condition of our half-deck made everything else seem trivial. On approaching the door we noticed that water was squirting out through the jamb on to the deck. Hitherto we had only known it to squirt inwards. It was a bad omen, for there could be but one explanation. The half-deck must be well filled with water. None was quite prepared for what met us when we opened the door to peep in.

Fortunately, I happened to be standing to one side when I released the latch, for the door crashed open. A deluge of water shot out, carrying with it what once had been a mattress, a sweeping-brush, a scrubbing-brush, various articles of clothing, a copy of *The Four Feathers*, together with several personal and treasured possessions, all of which promptly slithered across the main deck into the scuppers. As the scupper-holes were belching water overboard, we all rushed to try and retrieve valued belongings. I managed to secure a pipe, my only one, also a much-thumbed photograph of my sweetheart Daisy Green which was swirling around in a whirlpool over a scupper-hole. I pushed her up on top of my head under my sou'wester for safety but, alas, she never looked the same again.

We peered into the gloomy cavern of the half-deck. The sounds reminded me of the time I had explored a cave in a cliff at half-tide. There were gurglings and a sucking noise of water when the vessel rolled. Dimly we saw mattresses, bunk-boards, coats, caps, socks, and even shoes swilling around, appearing and disappearing as though in a boiling pot. The sea had even lifted the lids of our sea-chests and disgorged most of their contents. A sea came tumbling aboard, even as we watched, slithered up the outside of the half-deck and slopped some water through a gap between two of the steel platings beside Charlie's bunk.

"That explains some of it," he remarked, pointing towards the spouts coming through as though from a leaky hose. "The rivets have started."

"We'd better report it to the Old Man," said George. "We can't swim while we're asleep."

"Perhaps he'll find us berths somewhere in the saloon." Gogan was always optimistic.

Charlie snorted. "More likely to tell us to berth along with the crowd for'ard. There are some spare bunks in the fo'c'sle."

"That would be against the agreement made in our indentures," I protested. "They distinctly say that the apprentices are to have separate accommodation from the seamen."

"Indentures?" George looked at me contemptuously. "They are only worded one way, and that's to suit the Owners. What's the use of standing here? It's my watch below and only an hour of it left. I'm going to speak to the Old Man about it. We can't sleep in the half-deck, that's a certainty." Presently George came back with the news that the apprentices were to sleep in the sail-locker until the carpenter had a chance of sealing up the defective plates.

On the whole, we quite welcomed the idea. The sail-locker was under the poop and, although it was stuffy, and one could not stand up straight in it, and the tightly rolled canvas with its roping and big iron clews not exactly the ideal bed, it was dry. Dry? Why we had not known the luxurious meaning of that word for many months. The ship lurched through the night on her new course. Possibly, had not every one of us been so completely worn out, we would not have slept so well in a ship that only rolled half-way, and then in the opposite direction to the way she should go. "It seems unnatural-like," was a remark passed more than once in the fo'c'sle. The watch below, however, were past caring, and the watch on deck became resigned to it, if they did not get used to it.

Despite her handicap, the *Denbigh Castle* had placed eighty odd miles between herself and the Horn by daybreak next morning. The wind had moderated and, with it still on the quarter, the decks were comparatively free of water. At the first opportunity, we apprentices started to clear up the half-deck. Even after it had been baled out, sea-chests were oozing water, and family photographs and letters, so valued by the sailor, were an unrecognizable pulp. Poking into a dark corner I pulled out some slimy rags, to discover that they were part of my underwear.

In between our grumbling and lamentations we speculated on the captain's plans. "We're going to run the eastern down all right," said Charlie. "We wouldn't be steering north-east if we were going to Port Stanley."

"But why are we steering north-east?" queried George. "Why shouldn't we be steering east? That's our proper course."

"I bet we will all be mustered aft at eight bells," said Charlie. "The Old Man will have to tell the hands what he intends doing." He was right. At the changing of the watches, "Old Jowl's" whistle blew, to be followed by his familiar bellow for the hands to lay aft.

The men shambled aft with eager curiosity. The Old Man standing on the poop, hands clasped behind his back, looked moodily down upon them. Beside him stood "Old Jowl" and Mr. Owen. The crowd, shuffling their feet, waited expectantly.

"Men," his voice was strident; "as you can see for yourselves, we can no longer stay off the Horn. Winter is coming on, and what chance we had is gone now that the cargo has shifted. We will have to sail northwards until we get into finer weather and then see if we can trim the cargo to get the ship on to a more even keel. After that I intend running the eastern down."

"What about grub?" Kemp's high-pitched voice came from the back of the group.

"Well, I can't feed you on patent fuel, can I?" answered the Old Man testily. "We'll have to call in somewhere to replenish our stores, that's all."

"What port do you intend calling into, sir?" It was Mathews who spoke.

"That's my business," Captain Evans snapped. "Any more questions?"

"What are we goin' to do about clothes, Captain? Ours is wore out," said Kemp.

"You hadn't any when you stowed away in this ship," retorted the Old Man, "and it didn't worry you, my man." The hands tittered. "Anybody else got anything else to say?" The men remained silent. "Right. That's all."

"That'll do, the watch; relieve the wheel," and "Old Jowl" motioned a dismissal with a wave of his hand. The men went forward talking amongst themselves.

"What did he say about us trimmin' cargo?" demanded Kemp. "He can't do that on us when we ain't got no grub. All he can ask of us is to 'elp sail the ship to the nearest port."

"She mightn't get to de nearest port, de way she is," said Big Charlie. "It is not de pleasure-cruise runnin' de eastern down in de Roarin' Forties."

"We're all too soft, that's what's the matter with us," said Kemp warming to his pet subject. "When we get into port it will be 'yes, sir,' and 'aye, aye, sir,' instead of takin' an action against the Owners for breach of contrack. That's what it is, breach of contrack. We should go to law."

"You ask me anything, you'll be runnin' away from the law whenever you gets into port," said Mathews, with a grin.

"Well, what of it?" demanded Kemp defiantly, "what can one man do on his own? You'll all run away, too, the very first night you gets ashore. The captain will be a fine fellah because he advances you a quid instead of ten bob out of your hard-earned money, an' you will go into the pubs an' forget all the wrongs he's done you. An' after you've spent it all you'll come back on board. What for? To make more thousands of pounds for the bloomin' ship-owners who break their contrack, who starve you an' make you work like slaves. Bah!" and he spat contemptuously into the scuppers.

The men who, at the beginning of the passage, had either ignored him, made jocular and sceptical remarks or told him to "put a sock in it", now remained silent. The cruel battering they had received off the Horn had not yet been forgotten. The meagre food ration allowed them by the Board of Trade had been already drastically reduced, and months must still go by before they would be advanced their quid and given a night ashore. Throughout their lives they had mutely accepted the hardness of their fate which normally meant a four months' outward-bound passage, six weeks or so in port, and another four months to the final port of discharge where they would be paid off.

This voyage was different. In a vague way they felt that they were being cheated of their rights. Loyally and unthinkingly they had given of their best for the welfare of the ship, for far longer than four months, yet their reward was only increased hardship. The consoling axiom, "more days, more dollars," had lost most of its flavour, and Kemp, despite his shortcomings, seemed to be able to put thoughts into words. Under existing circumstances, their minds were fertile for discontent.

.   .   .   .

The *Denbigh Castle*, every sail set except the royals, jogged along quietly before a gentle breeze. A welcome sun shone down and outlined her sails in shadow upon a blue sea. She had found fine weather in latitude 38 degrees and was now heading east. The hatches had been removed from the three hatchways and our watch was employed trimming the cargo. The patent fuel with which we were loaded took the form of bricks, each roughly the size and weight of four ordinary house bricks, and composed of coal-dust and tar mixed with some chemical. The open hatchways showed that many of them had tumbled over to the port side, indeed some of the cargo might have shifted bodily when the ship had been thrown to such an acute angle by the great wave. For two days now we had been passing the bricks from the port to the starboard side. There was just enough room for the men to crawl between the top of the cargo and the deck above them. The bricks had to be passed singly from hand to hand, and soon our hands and finger-nails were torn and broken.

At noon, our watch on deck finished, Charlie, Gogan and I sat down on deck, faces and arms as black from the dust as though we had been working coal. Suddenly my skin began to burn as though I were sitting too close to a fire. "Dashed funny," I remarked, "but my skin feels as though it were on fire." Both Charlie and Gogan said that they, too, felt the same. Next thing we found that our eyes were streaming water. Everybody who had been working down the hole was suffering from the same complaint. Chips had succeeded in stopping the leak in our half-deck to which we adjourned to get out of the sun.

"The sooner we wash this stuff off, the better," said Charlie. Our water was strictly rationed but we had collected some rain-water to replenish a cask for the purpose, lashed in the corner of the half-deck. It smelt rather strongly but we were not in a position to be fastidious. To our surprise, the dirt refused to be washed off. The tar or chemical responsible for our discomfort seemed to have become ingrained in our skin.

"Say, what the devil can we do about it?" groaned Gogan. "This burning and itchiness is driving me crazy."

"I imagine grease is the only remedy," Charlie replied. "I'll ask Cookie to give us some. He's got a cask full of it under the fo'c'sle head." Any grease that a cook could save on board a sailing-ship was always his perquisite. At the end of a voyage he could always get quite a price for it from a ship chandler.

"We'll come with you," Gogan and I exclaimed, and we went to the galley and showed the cook the condition of our faces and arms.

"It's very strange, I must say," said Cookie peering at us through his reading glasses.

"A spot of grease should do it good," said Charlie. "What about giving us some out of your cask?"

"That grease, it's valuable, look you. It means quite a bit for me at the end of the voyage. Still, I suppose I had better let you have a little, but only a little, mind you."

"Say, look!" I exclaimed. All hands seemed to have forestalled Charlie's idea and were lathering their faces and arms with Cookie's grease. "Only a little, look you," said Gogan imitating the cook's voice as we dipped our arms into the cask. We smelt abominably but it removed the dirt and eased the irritation.

"Well, thank goodness for that," remarked Gogan, after we had returned to the half-deck. "A good idea of yours about the grease, Charlie. Hello! What's going on?" We paused to listen. A stream of language, half English, half Welsh, came floating from for'ard.

"It's the cook!" exclaimed Charlie. "He's found out that all hands have been digging into his grease cask. Let's go and see the fun." The cook, in a furious passion, was standing with both arms outstretched above his head, and calling down curses upon the semicircle of grinning men who stood around him. Suddenly his flow was cut short by a handful of grease flung unerringly at his open mouth, followed by another, and another, until his face was plastered. In a towering rage, he retired amidst the jeers and laughs of the crowd. He came to the break of the poop, where the captain and "Old Jowl" were standing, and still spluttering with anger, called out to them, "My grease, look you! Those thieves for'ard have stolen half a barrel! Never before have I been treated so!" He wiped some of the grease off his beard with his fingers and flicked it on the deck.

It is to the credit of Captain Evans that he did not laugh. His mouth twitched momentarily, and his shoulders jerked a couple of times as though the effort to conceal his emotion was almost too much for him, but he did not laugh. Nobody could tell what took place beneath "Old Jowl's" moustache but he succeeded in turning an explosive splutter into a fair imitation of a cough.

"What's the matter with you, Cook?" the Old Man demanded sternly.

"My grease!" the cook called out excitedly. "Those sons of . . . I mean the men for'ard have stolen the cask of grease I kept for'ard, Captain. I've been saving it so careful, spoonful by spoonful I put into that cask, and now . . ." He waved his arms in and out from his sides helplessly.

"Where did the grease come from?"

"Why, sir, from the galley, of course. Ever since the passage began, I've been saving it, spoonful by spoonful. . . ."

"Have you saved it from the meals made by you for the crew?"

"Why, yes, sir." The cook looked rather puzzled at these apparently stupid questions.

The Old Man put his hands on the rail and looked down at the cook. "Now, listen to me. If the grease is over from the crew's meals, they are entitled to it if they want it."

"But," answered the cook, "it has always been the practice, sir, for the cook to have the grease, and . . ."

"There's nothing about it in the articles you signed."

"I know, I know," and an appealing note crept into his voice, "but it has always been the custom, look you."

"Those kind of customs have nothing to do with me," snapped the captain. "What do you want me to do? Do you expect me to go and guard your grease with a belaying-pin in my hand?"

"No, sir, of course not, only I thought that you might tell the men that they are not to steal my grease. Spoonful by spoonful I've saved it, mind you."

"They are not stealing. You've told me it's from their dinners, so that's all there is to it. Right, that'll do."

A sound, almost like a groan, came from the cook's lips as he turned towards his galley. "Wait." It was "Old Jowl" who spoke. "Wash that grease off the deck before somebody slips on it." Poor Cookie. There was moisture in his eyes as, muttering audibly, he carried out the mate's order. We did not know what he was saying. He raved in Welsh.

The "perks" aboard ships is a strictly tricky subject. The mate also had perquisites in the form of rope-yarns and old rope which we boys had to collect for him and stow into sacks. They fetched quite a high price when sold at the end of the voyage. The captain was fully aware, unofficially, of these customs, but it was very unwise of the cook to bring the matter of the grease to his notice as it placed the captain in a false position. Having been given the information, he could have told the cook that he would have to commandeer the grease and send the proceeds of its sale to the owners as a "left-over" from the provisions supplied by them.

After seven days in the hold, the trimming of the cargo was completed, but the cargo had shifted bodily for, although we had built it higher on the starboard side, securing it by shifting-boards, the ship still rolled heavier to port than to starboard. Nevertheless, we had greatly improved her seaworthiness, and replaced the hatches.

The ship continued her passage to the eastward in about latitude 38 degrees.

We made poor progress due to light airs and variable winds. For two whole days we lay becalmed, the big fore-and-aft mainsails, hanging from the hauled-up bunt-lines to prevent chaffing, kicking and flapping helplessly as they wallowed languidly in the lazy swell. Then one morning before dawn, a light air came whispering from the east, and ahead, to catch her all aback. Sharp orders from "Old Jowl", and the blocks gave tongue as the yards were braced close up on the port tack, and the ship sailed south as though seeking to find some invisible gap through which she could penetrate to the westward. The shortage of food became practically the sole topic of conversation in both fo'c'sles.

Kemp lost no opportunities to fan the discontent. "Haven't I been tellin' you all along that this 'ere capting doesn't know his job? An' all the replies I got was that I don't know nothink. Wait until the grub runs out, that's all! We should take charge of the ship ourselves before it's too late."

I discussed the situation with my old confidant, Paddy. Being a sailor of experience, his opinions would remain unaltered by those of the fo'c'sle, and least of all by Kemp's clap-trap.

"In the Forties? Not at all," he said in reply to my query. "I've run the eastern down dozens of times. Why there you get roaring' westerly winds with everything crackin' and strainin' up aloft, an' the hands standin' by the halliards three an' four times in a watch for days on end. But nobody ever cared. Sailors can't expect to have flying-fish weather all the time, an' the harder their ship is driven the quicker the passage and nights ashore to follow."

"But what do you think is the reason that we're not in the Forties?" I asked.

Paddy looked around at the horizon for inspiration. "It's not for the likes of me to say. I've never criticized me captains. This Ol' Man may think the ship is not fit for the weather in the Forties. Again, his health and nerves may have suffered after all we've been through. It's all very well for the likes of us to talk. We've only got to obey orders, but it's the man what gives the orders who has the worry."

"But what's he going to do if the provisions run out?"

"There you are again; that's the captain's responsibility. When you get your certificates and become a second mate, and then mate and captain, you'll find that the higher you go the more responsibility you have, and the more worry along with it."

As the weeks passed, the shortage of food became more and more acute until, finally, there was nothing to eat on board except biscuits. They were about three inches square and about half an inch thick. Consequently, a biscuit washed down with only water made hard going for both teeth and stomach. Many and various were the ways we treated the biscuit to try and make it more appetizing. In fact it became quite a ritual. First a corner was broken off which, having been burnt black in the oven, was ground into a powder. Having poured boiling water

on it, we called the concoction "coffee" at breakfast-time, and
"tea" for supper.

Strangely enough, the least perturbed person on board
seemed to be the Old Man. The day came when he appeared on
deck and, having looked around at the horizon, said, "reduce
sail down to lower topsails, Mr. Jones."

The men received the order with consternation. "The Ol'
Man must be off his bloomin' rocker . . . no grub aboard an'
reduce to lower topsails with a fair wind! . . . it ain't sense,"
while above the angry comments could be heard Kemp's shrill
voice, "Don't take in his sail for him! Why should we starve
for a man what's off his blinkin' chump?"

"Man those bunt-lines and cut off the cackle!" "Old Jowl"
stumped up, with his stiff leg thumping on the deck. Mechanically, we pulled on the bunt- and clew-lines but the pulling was
done in silence except for an occasional grunt or a "now".

The absence of the cheery "Yah hays" was always a marked
indication of unrest amongst the crew. A captain or his mates
could never order us to give these sing-song cries, so essential
for speeding up the work. They could retaliate, however, with
very good effect by "hazing" the offenders, or keeping them
sweating on the braces, swigging on all the halliards and setting
up taut all the sheets until the spirit of antagonism was subdued through the sheer weariness of their bodies.

The *Denbigh Castle* lurched sullenly along. Her very appearance seemed to reflect an air of dejection. Her naked masts
waved protestingly across the sky as though appealing for sail to
be set when the wind was fair. The patches of green weed on
her decks which, as Paddy jocularly remarked to me, "needed
trimming with a lawn mower", made her look as though she
were a derelict. Big patches of yellow rust exuded from the
tropical blisters on her paintwork. Her brasswork, which had

formerly glittered from elbow-grease, bathbrick and oil, was now salt-stained and mildewed. Here and there on the rigging and stays, serving and parcelling had come adrift to flutter disconsolately as "Irishmen's pennants" in the wind.

The discontentment on board was not confined to the fo'c'sle. The steward, in rather a plaintive voice, was unburdening his troubles to the cook. ". . . Thought he was goin' to strike me, I did, an' all I did was to apologize for servin' the same food for dinner as I'd served for the breakfast. 'You keep your mouth shut,' 'e says, 'an' attend to your work.' Me attend to me work? An' me slavin' all day keepin' them cabins clean, although I'm on short rations like everybody else. Ask me anything, the man's going barmy."

"I can tell you what was the matter, look you," and the cook stooped to put a spill in the fire to light his pipe. "The Old Man knows that he is unpopular because he has taken in sail. When you started talking about the grub, he thought you were having a dig at him, see. That's because we are short of grub and he should set more sail. He is sort of touchy about it and is only waiting to jump on anybody he thinks is criticizing him."

The steward scratched his head. "'Old Jowl' hardly spoke to 'im throughout the meal . . . just said something about the crowd needing careful handling, an' the Old Man just replied that a spell of hazing 'em wouldn't do any 'arm. Then the mate says, 'if you tire the men out that way, what with the shortage of grub an' such-like, they won't be strong enough to take in sail.' With that the Old Man whips round on 'im and says, 'the sail is already in, Mr. Evans', an' up he jumps an' goes in to his cabin. Lord, you should 'ave 'eard the way he banged the door. 'Old Jowl' just looked at the door an' gave his shoulders a bit of a shrug-like. Queer goings-on, I must say."

I was just going back to the half-deck with my news when I

saw Kemp coming from for'ard, his face for once looking smug. Instinctively feeling that there might be more news in the offing, I turned towards a belaying-pin opposite the galley door and started recoiling one of the bunt-lines.

"Mornin', Stewy," said Kemp lounging against the galley doorway and, to my surprise, held out a dirty envelope to the steward. "You're to give this 'ere billy ducks to the Ol' Man. It's from the 'ands with their compliments, as you might say."

"An' when did you start givin' me orders?" demanded the steward heatedly.

"I ain't givin' you any orders," said Kemp. "I'm only obeyin' me instructions, I am. The 'ands told me what to do 'an I'm adoing it, see? 'Give this 'ere note to the steward,' they said, 'an' tell him to see that the Ol' Man gets it.' An' I don't mind tellin' yeh," and Kemp leaned forward confidentially, "I wouldn't offend the 'ands, if I was you. They ain't in what you might call an 'appy mood, if you gets me meanin'."

Reluctantly the steward took the envelope. "What's it all about, anyway?"

Kemp put his forefinger to one side of his nose and shut his right eye expressively. "All in good time, Stewy; you'll find out quick enough when you 'ands the envelope to the Ol' Man."

Not waiting to hear any more, I hurried along to the half-deck. "Say, you chaps," I exclaimed, "the hands for'ard are up to something or other." Triumphantly I told them what I had overheard. News was scarce aboard the *Denbigh Castle*. We almost knew what the other was going to say before he opened his mouth.

"It can hardly be a letter of complaint," said Charlie. "Who ever heard of a crew writing a letter to their captain? They always muster aft and ask to see him."

"If you ask me anything," George began . . . but we never

heard what he was going to say. He was interrupted by a shrill blast from the mate's whistle followed by a yell, "Lay aft, all hands!"

"Now we'll learn all about it," said Gogan as we all trooped out on deck. The men stood in front of the poop murmuring to one another. Occasionally there was a forced laugh to camouflage the uneasiness a crew usually experience when about to be interviewed by their captain. The average sailing-ship man was not as a rule an expert in expressing his views to his superior, no matter how just his cause might be. The captain might twist the speaker's words so as to make the complaint unanswerable, leaving the unfortunate complainant dumb and frustrated. The Old Man kept them waiting, knowing that it would be a silent reminder of his exalted status as well as having a detrimental effect on the morale of the men who had keyed themselves up in the fo'c'sle. "Old Jowl" and Mr. Owen stood on the poop talking in undertones and glancing occasionally at the chart-room door.

Suddenly the Old Man appeared on the poop and looked at the compass as though oblivious of the men mustered on the main deck. He glanced around the horizon and upwards at the gaunt masts swinging lazily to and fro overhead. At length he advanced towards the break of the poop and, putting his hand into his side-pocket, drew out the envelope which, as everybody noted, had already been opened. He extracted the contents with his forefinger and thumb. They consisted of two small white feathers taken from the breast of an albatross.

Although weather-beaten, his skin was sallow, and his eyes were sunken and bloodshot. Holding up the two emblems he looked down at the expectant crowd and then said, "Now, men, what is all this?" There was a silence for about ten seconds and then Mathews advanced in front of the group. "It's like this, 'ere, sir. Me an' me mates have been talkin' things over like, an' we all thinks that you're showin' the white feather, that you're scared to set sail on the ship."

Mathews paused, but the murmur of appreciation from the men encouraged him to continue. "'Ere we are, short of grub and the baccy just finished. We've got a fair wind, yet look at what we've got set up aloft!" The hands all glanced upwards as Mathews dramatically pointed his finger. "Three lower topsails, sir, that's all, three lower topsails. As sailormen we feel that the ship should 'ave every rag set, the circumstances bein' what they are."

The veins on the Old Man's forehead stood out but he controlled his temper. "I see that you and your malcontents have been reading Mason's *Four Feathers*. I didn't know I had shipped such a crowd of educated seamen. And just because you can spell out a few words, you think you are qualified to handle the ship for me, is that it?" The men looked at him sullenly but nobody replied, and the captain went on, "I suppose it was too much of an effort to spell out to the end of the story and so find out that those four feathers were the greatest injustice ever done to any man, and that's what I think of the two feathers you have given me now." The Old Man released his fingers and let the feathers blow away in the wind.

Mathews stood nonplussed, and then Turner called out, "What we want is more sail set on the ship. We want no fancy talks. Let's get the ship into port!" A loud murmur of assent arose from the others. "That's it . . . we want sail set . . . no grub . . . no baccy . . . get the sails on her!"

The Old Man's face turned scarlet. "I'm responsible for the safety of the ship," he shouted. "She's in bad trim and the barometer is down below twenty-nine. It can blow up a gale within an hour."

"What if it does blow, Captain?" It was Big Charlie who

spoke. "You haf a goot crowd of sailormens on board. You order de sails to be set an' we'll take 'em in for you when de time comes. Dat's fair enough, ain't it?" A cheer from the hands followed this speech, upon which the Old Man lost his temper completely.

"Right!" he roared. "Set everything! Put the royals on her as well, and I hope the ship sinks under the lot of you! It's all you deserve!" Then, turning on his heel, he walked into the chart-room.

The men stood dumbfounded at this outburst. Some of the older hands shook their heads dubiously; some even remarked that he must be ill. Other remarks such as, "He's gone crackers . . . off his chump," were passed from one to the other. They shuffled their feet uncomfortably. Their request had been granted and they had been given a free hand to carry it out, yet now they did not know what to do. The more superstitious of them felt that, although they had been given permission to set sail, it might bring bad luck in view of what the captain had said. Perhaps the gale might blow the ship under before the sail could be taken in again. It was like setting it under a curse.

"Old Jowl", however, had no such misgivings. With a shout that sounded almost enthusiastic he called out, "What are you men hangin' around for? All hands remain on deck; starboard watch take the foremast, port watch, the main! Up aloft, you boys, and loose those upper topsails. You ask for sail to be set an' then you hang around like a gang of hoboes! Lively now, lively! Take your topsails halliards to the capstan!"

The men needed no further urging. Enthusiastically they ran to carry out the orders. "Good 'Old Jowl' . . . should be in charge he should." Men clambered up aloft along with us boys and laid out along the yards where they threw off the gaskets. Others hurried along the deck bringing with them long capstan bars taken from their rack, and fitted them into the sockets around the capstan-heads in readiness to walk around and so heave up the heavy topsail yards. Once again the familiar working cries echoed throughout the ship, and gradually lofty and swaying pyramids of white canvas were built up, sail by sail, even to the royals.

The ship seemed to awaken from a trance. Her sails bellied out into graceful curves, the contours filled with driving wind. Her stern lifted happily, her bow bored determinedly into the water to churn it into a welter of foam, and a wave from each bow danced away obliquely across the sea. Speckled white water streamed aft along each side of her hull to mingle with her wake which finally dissolved itself astern.

The *Denbigh Castle* lived again.

CHAPTER SEVEN

ECLIPSE OF KEMP

THE gale foretold by the captain never materialized. The wind strengthened next day but the Old Man ordered only the royals and upper t'gallant sails to be taken in, and for several days the ship lurched and rolled ahead at a steady nine knots. At first Kemp strutted about as though he alone were responsible for the success of the recent interview with the Old Man. "What did I tell youse?" he repeated several times a day. "If we 'adn't complained we'd be a thousand miles astern today." The men kept silent. Eager for praise, he foolishly ventured further. "I 'opes as 'ow you realize that it was a good thing you took me advice."

Big Charlie, who was pulling off his sea-boot, looked up. "Vot did you say?"

"You 'eard me, didn't yer? I says that if you 'adn't taken me advice we'd be a thousand miles astern now."

"You give advice?" and Big Charlie sent a jet of clear saliva into the bogie stove.

This infuriated Kemp. "Yes, you big square-head." His high voice became shrill. "You'd never 'ave the brains; yer blinkin' mind doesn't rise above pullin' on a rope."

Slowly and methodically Big Charlie started to pull on his sea-boot again. His movements were so deliberate that Kemp failed to anticipate trouble. The sea-boot on, to his satisfaction, Charlie stamped his foot and advanced. Too late to make an escape through the door, Kemp backed up against the side of the fo'c'sle. "Don't you dare touch me!" and a note of alarm crept into his voice. "I'll 'ave the law on yer when we gets into port, see?" Inexorably the Russian Finn continued his advance. "You can't do it . . . you've no right. . . ." His voice died away in a whimper as Big Charlie's right hand shot out suddenly and, gripping the clothes on Kemp's chest in a massive clutch, held him out at arm's length. "Let me go . . . let me go." With arms flailing Kemp also endeavoured to kick his opponent's shins.

Most of the men were in their bunks, and they leaned up on their elbows to watch. Big Charlie studied his victim like a boa-constrictor with a rabbit. His left arm went behind his back, to reappear with a sheath-knife. Kemp screamed, his eyes dilating in terror. The Finn shook the scream out of him, dog-fashion, and then pointed the knife an inch off his throat. "You little cockroach. You bit of vind an' bilgewater," he growled. "You takes back dose verds or . . ." and the knife scraped Kemp's throat.

"Charlie . . . for the love of . . . I'm sorry. I didn't mean . . ." With a flick of his wrist Big Charlie flung the terrified wretch on his back where he lay for a few seconds before scrambling into his bunk. His narrow-set eyes watched his assailant as he went to bed. Suddenly, as soon as he saw Big Charlie safely turned in, he called out, "That ends it, mates; never no more will yous get any 'elp from me."

Big Charlie, who was too soft-hearted to kill a cockroach even when it ran across his pillow, smiled tolerantly in the darkness.

About a fortnight after the Kemp incident, Hans went mad. The first inkling of anything wrong was the thundering noise of kicking, thrashing canvas as the vessel was taken aback. We ran out on deck to see the sails struggling furiously for release from their sheets while the yards themselves jerked so violently that the very masts trembled. The curve of the wake showed that the ship was turning right up against the wind into a tumbling sea. A ship travelling at about eight knots, to be steered up into the teeth of a strong breeze and lumpy sea, can run into trouble. The placing of the rigging is such that it leans slightly behind the masts, the better to withstand the pressure of the wind on the sails. Consequently, should the wind come on the wrong side of the sails, all the strain is taken up by the very much lighter fore and aft stays and, should they snap, the masts could fall backwards if the ship pitched heavily into a head sea.

The pandemonium up aloft made the watch below come tumbling out on deck even before "Old Jowl" had time to blow his whistle. The men had not forgotten their assurance to the Old Man that they would be prepared for any emergency while there was plenty of sail set. They stood by the braces, for in such circumstances it is by the position of the sails and yards that the ship is brought once more under control. Were such a situation to arise with a toy ship in a bath, its owner would push the bow around with his finger until the sails filled again. The master of a sailing-ship performs the same act in principle, that of putting pressure forward and reducing it aft, only instead of using his finger, he uses the wind. The yards for'ard are trimmed so as to catch the full force of the wind, while the after-yards are directed so that the wind on the sails has little or no effect. Consequently the vessel must "pay off" and bring the wind abeam or astern as required.

"Old Jowl" came clumping along the deck, dot-and-dash fashion as Paddy described it, followed by Mr. Owen, to slack away the braces on one side while we hauled away on the other. Even as we hauled, one could hear the men, in low tones, commenting and speculating among themselves. "Who's at the wheel? . . . Hans, wasn't it? . . . The helm must have been put hard down, whoever it was. . . . Perhaps the Old Man . . . why, there's Hans!" Simultaneously all eyes turned to look at Hans, with his lumbering walk, coming for'ard. A Swede by nationality, he was short, thick-set and, although only about thirty years of age, his hair and eyelashes were almost white. Although too taciturn to be popular, he was appreciated as a good seaman who never shirked his work.

"Heh, Hans, what 'as happened? Did you imagine you were steerin' a steamer, puttin' 'er into the wind?" So far as Hans was concerned, the men might never have existed. With his thumbs stuck into his belt, his face utterly unemotional, he lurched past the men and disappeared through the fo'c'sle door.

"Another hand to the wheel!" It was Mr. Owen who spoke. The wheel? Nobody had relieved Hans, but somebody must be there. Eagerly we obeyed "Old Jowl's" order to shift to the mizzen braces from where we could see aft. Standing on the little platform holding the spokes, stood the Old Man! "Come on, whose wheel is it?" demanded Mr. Owen.

"I was to relieve Hans at eight bells, sir," answered Fritz.

"Well, get along there right away," and Fritz had to take his trick out of turn. The yards trimmed at length to the satisfaction of "Old Jowl", the men hastened for'ard to bombard Hans with questions. "What 'appened to you, Hans? Did the Old Man chase you? . . . 'ow did you get her caught aback?"

The Swede turned and seemed to look at some distant object over our shoulders. "I vant to steer north," he answered. "I vant to steer north to catch some vish for food."

"Steer north to catch some fish for food?" echoed Turner in amazement. "Blimey!" Yet despite all their questioning, that was the only reply they could get from Hans. Obviously his brain was affected. Later we learnt further details, through our usual channel of information, the galley news. Mr. Owen, who was on watch at the time, had gone down below for a moment and, during his absence, Hans put the wheel hard down. As the vessel turned up into the wind with a thunderous flapping of the canvas, the captain, mates and the steward had rushed up from the saloon. "Put that helm up, you fool!" bellowed the Old Man, but the Swede simply ignored him. Thereupon the captain jumped on to the platform and grasping the spokes himself, shouldered Hans away. "What the devil do you think you're doing?"

"I vant to steer north to catch vish for vood."

"Heaven's above!" exclaimed the master. "Get for'ard out of this! Call all hands," and he turned to the two mates. "And get those yards trimmed. This chap's gone looney."

The men were suspicious of their unfortunate shipmate at first. Big Charlie in fact thought it wiser to remove the Swede's sheath-knife which, incidentally, he never appeared to miss. Poor Hans proved to be harmless. He mooned listlessly around the deck, sometimes gazing out at the horizon for long periods at a time. The officers ignored him and when the men spoke to him it was as though they were speaking to a child. There was one occasion, however, when Hans created a diversion.

Among his possessions, Sails had a collection of about a dozen harpoons which he prized highly. Often, in the tropics, he would arouse our admiration at his dexterity in catching fish in this manner. Many an hour he spent in the dog-watch polishing and greasing them. On this particular day, it was in the afternoon watch, we suddenly heard appealing cries of "Stop him! Stop him!" The voice was that of old Sails. Immediately thoughts of Hans sprang to our minds and we jumped to our feet and ran for the door. Had Hans suddenly become violent? Perhaps he was trying to murder the poor old sailmaker! Even half the watch below were tumbling out on deck as we boys hurried for'ard. We found that Hans was indeed the cause

94

of the commotion but fortunately not in the way we had anticipated.

Apparently, Sails had been cleaning his harpoons and had left them leaning against the fife-rail to fetch some grease. They had been found by Hans who had taken them to clamber out on to the end of the jib-boom. Sails had returned and, to his horror, had found him hurling his precious harpoons at imaginary fish. Unfortunately, from the sailmaker's point of view, Hans had omitted to fit any connecting-lines and the harpoons were lost for ever. They were all gone before any action could be taken, always assuming that anybody had felt inclined to tackle a demented man sitting at the end of a jib-boom armed with harpoons.

"What did he want to do that for?" queried old Sails appealing to the others.

"He wanted to catch some vish for vood," replied my friend Paddy, with a sly grin.

Jokes, however, were few now on board the *Denbigh Castle*. Shortage of food and tobacco, and the fact that we were heartily sick of the sight of one another, deprived us of conversation, let alone a sense of humour. To make things even more gloomy, we had now run out of paraffin oil.

During the second dog-watches when we would have been reading, mending clothes or perhaps having a game of cards, there was nothing to do now but lie on our bunks, and think. During the changing of the night-watches we had to go to bed and get up in the dark. We sailed through the nights without any navigation lights burning. True, there was oil in these lamps so that they could be lighted in an emergency should another ship be sighted but, alas, we never saw any other ships.

It was galley news which suddenly burst upon us like a stop press edition of a paper giving vital information which could affect the whole world. A cheer from the fo'c'sle was the first intimation we boys had of something startling.

"Say!" demanded Gogan excitedly, "what's struck them for'ard? They cheered! Why, there hasn't been a bleat out of them for weeks!"

"Something's up, all right," said George. "Let's slip round to the galley and see if the cook knows anything." We all trooped around to the galley door.

"What's in the air, Cookie?" George demanded.

The cook looked at us blankly. "I do not know what you mean. Is it that you cannot speak the proper English, look you?"

"We heard the hands cheering for'ard," I exclaimed. "Whatever for?"

"How would I know?" and the cook turned to shift a pot on the stove. "I do not go into the fo'c'sle whatever."

It would have been fatal to let him see that we could have shaken him out of sheer exasperation. "Come on, Cookie," pleaded Gogan, "spill it."

"It might have been something I said to Fritz just now as he was coming from the wheel, but then, mind you, it was only gossip as you might say." The cook was enjoying keeping us all on tenterhooks.

"What was it? What did you tell him?" we demanded eagerly.

"Oh, it is not of much importance, mind you. And there may not be any truth in it whatever, but the steward happened to hear the captain tell the mate that the wind was more suitable to steer for Fremantle instead of Albany, and if it held, we should sight land in a couple of days."

"Fremantle in a couple of days!" The cook grinned as he watched our astonished faces. For months the arrival in a port had been something which, we hoped, would eventually

Leaping for the life-line

The main deck awash

Above: Men straddling extremities of the yard

Left: A bird's eye view from 175 feet

materialize in the dim and distant future, something we had worked and slaved for, yet it had begun to seem like getting to Heaven when we died.

When my watch below came, I lay dazedly in my bunk. Fremantle. The magic name meant food. It meant bacon and eggs, roast beef, bread and butter, vegetables. I would be able to send a letter home. The very word, "home", suddenly became clear and real. I saw the little postman with his big black moustache walking up the front path and giving his familiar tat-tat-tat on the knocker. Possibly, in view of the fact that the letter had a stamp from "foreign parts" he might ring and say to my mother, "Axin' your pardon, Ma'm, but would the letter be from young master Albert by any chance?" Such a query from a country village postman in Ireland would not be made out of idle curiosity, nor considered presumptuous. Undoubtedly, everybody in the little village of Dundrum, where my parents lived, knew I was missing and sympathized silently if not openly with my family. In fact, my mother told me afterwards that people, whom she had never spoken to before, stopped her in the road to congratulate her upon the good news.

I would write, too, to Daisy. It might put a spoke in the wheel of that chap, Edwards, whom I always suspected had his eye on her. How small he would feel if she told him she had received a letter from me, and gave him an outline of my adventures. How strange, to think that I had not seen, let alone spoken, to a girl for over eighteen months. Truly this visit to Fremantle was going to be the most outstanding day of my life since I had first kissed Daisy on the forehead.

CHAPTER EIGHT

PORT

"PADDY."
            "Sir?"

"Slip up to the fore royal and see if you can see any land ahead. Here, take these binoculars." Since I had joined the *Denbigh Castle* I don't suppose I obeyed an order from Mr. Owen with greater willingness. I stood on the royal-yard, my arm curled round the mast and studied the horizon, piecemeal fashion, first with my naked eye, and then with the binoculars. "You won't see anything," I told myself. "It would just be too wonderful a thing to happen." Alas, my words were true. The interminable line of the horizon, so long the circumference of my life, remained unbroken.

After an hour, Mr. Owen called me down. "Never mind, Paddy, there's always tomorrow."

"I'm glad to hear you say that, sir," I replied rather bitterly. "In this ship tomorrow always seems the same as today."

Shortly after dawn next morning, Taffy Jones, who was on the look-out, reported land ahead! Land! This was no galley buzz. It hit us like the report from a gun. Had some extra-ordinary marine monster been sighted, the men could not have hurried more quickly on to the fo'c'sle head to view this "phenomenon" called land. The wild current of excitement, in some mysterious fashion, communicated itself to the watch below, and half-dressed and sleepy-eyed, they tumbled out on deck to crane over the rail. "That's no land, them is clouds . . .

garn, whoever saw a cloud like that . . . didn't Cookie say we might see land today . . . it vos de land all right." Excitedly, sceptically they argued, many of them afraid to admit to themselves that the hope of months was about to be realized.

It looked as though some artist of nature had rubbed out part of the horizon and, in the gap, drawn a faint irregular line with a pencil. How little it was to look at, yet most of us remained on deck frequently to crane our necks and gaze for'ard to convince ourselves that our eyes were not deceiving us.

The unseen artist who had sketched the first pencil line continued his work on the picture. Details were gently painted in, such as distant fields and trees. Other markings showed which might have been rocks or the roofs of houses, and presently a white pillar-shaped object became visible which Big Charlie, who had been to Fremantle before, announced as the lighthouse on Rotnest Island.

A blast from "Old Jowl's" whistle suddenly interrupted our sight-seeing. "Port watch, get the anchor cables up; starboard watch, rig the fish tackle and unlash the anchors."

The *Denbigh Castle* hastened landwards helped by a momentary freshening of the wind. Our pulses quickened as we gazed at the green fields and pastures, the scattered cottages and houses.

"Vessel coming out of the bay, sir!" the look-out man called.

The Old Man snatched up the telescope again and peered through it. "The pilot-boat," he muttered as he shut the glass with a snap. "Have that pilot-ladder ready," he called out to "Old Jowl", "and have the hands ready to back the mainyard!"

Never had the approach of a pilot-vessel been watched with greater interest. As proved by the newspaper reports after our arrival, the ship, in turn, created quite a sensation in Fremantle. She had been at sea over eight and a half months, a longer period on a passage than any other sailing-ship within memory. Her insurance at Lloyds, London, had soared towards ninety guineas instead of the ordinary ten or twelve, an ominous indication that the insurance brokers never expected to hear of her again. And now she had suddenly appeared thousands of miles from her destination.

"Back th' main-yard!" shouted the Old Man. Cheerily we hauled away on the weather main-brace until the great big main-sail was taken aback and the ship's speed in consequence reduced to a couple of knots. The pilot-boat, *Lady Forest*, manœuvred alongside.

Had Pilot Cleary been a visitor from another planet, he could not have been examined with greater interest by us all. Thirty pairs of eyes were focused upon him. Mr. Owen received him, as he clambered nimbly over the rail and jumped down on deck, and then accompanied him to the poop.

"Trim the main-yard!" The pilot shouted the order through a megaphone. All hands laid exuberantly on to the lee-brace.

"Haul away, men, haul away!" shouted "Old Jowl" who was standing by the weather brace ready to slack away.

"Valk her up, boys, valk her up!" called out Big Charlie. "There's plenty of us here." The men took up the words, "Yes, walk her up," and turning about, they stamped and cheered along the deck hauling the big yard around as they went until it was filled with the wind again. Once more the *Denbigh Castle* gathered way and hastened towards the entrance of the bay. The wind being fair, the pilot dispensed with the services of a tug.

The t'gallant and fore- and main-sails had to be taken in and given a neat harbour stow, and the topsail halliards had to be specially coiled down "clear for running" so that they would not become fouled at the crucial moment when the order came "Lower Away". The mate, accompanied by Chips armed with a big maul, stood by on the fo'c'sle head ready to knock the pin out which would let go the anchor. The pilot must have been surprised at the alacrity with which any order was carried out. Unless he had undergone our actual experience, it was difficult for him to understand the extraordinary feeling of elation which possessed us, "as tho'," in Paddy's words, "we all had had a double tot of rum."

"Lower away upper topsails!" We jumped to the downhauls and bunt-lines and, as Mr. Owen slackened away on the halliards, the yards came down with a run. "Up aloft and stow," ordered the second mate, and we raced up the rigging. From aloft I could see the ship making a graceful semicircle as the helm was put down and she swung up into the wind to finally lose her way and stop.

"Let go starboard anchor!" It was the most wonderful order we had heard since leaving Cardiff. Bang, thump, wallop, went Chippy's maul. Splash! And the anchor disappeared amidst a dollop of spray while Chips sprang to the windlass control-lever to check the cable running out in a cloud of rust-coloured dust. He tightened up the brake as the ship's head swung away. Gradually the anchor chain tautened to stretch out straight and unyielding into the water ahead, digging the anchor into the sea-bed.

The bows of the vessel, in response to the strain, swung into the wind. After being 253 days at sea, a record for any sailing-ship, she had come to rest.

I looked around me almost in wonderment. Glancing at the poop, I felt there was something missing, and suddenly realized that it was the man at the wheel. Since leaving Cardiff, that wheel had never been without a man standing beside it, his hands on the spokes. Even when the helmsman was being relieved at four and eight bells, be it in the day or the night, in calm or in storm, that wheel had never for an instant been without human touch, for his successor, advancing from behind, grasped the spokes before the other released his hold. Apart from this method being a time-honoured ritual, it is carried out from necessity. Seldom does a sailing-ship carry her rudder "dead centre" and, in consequence, there is nearly always pressure on the rudder which, in turn, puts pressure on the wheel. The wheel "kicks" with the rising and falling of the stern, and if released, might spin around and throw the vessel off her course. John Masefield refers to "the wheel's kick and the wind's song", in his poem, "Sea Fever". Now the wheel looked lonely, almost crestfallen.

Looking up aloft, I stared at the yards. For months I had not seen them without some sail set. The masts, looking gaunt and bare, stood motionless, as though hoping not to attract attention to themselves because they were ashamed of their nakedness. And then there was the wind, actually blowing direct from the fo'c'sle head along the deck. The effect was positively unnatural. The *Denbigh Castle* was no longer at sea.

One of the most tantalizing of situations is to sit in front of a big feed of roast beef, potatoes and cabbage, after half a year of starvation, and not be able to eat it.

Here it was, the food that we had talked about for months previously; the food that, in our dreams, we had eaten time and time again, only to awaken to the inevitable biscuit. We sat gloating over our plates, and then, suddenly, the dreadful truth dawned upon me. I could not eat it. How willing was the spirit but the stomach, alas, was weak. I forced a little meat down, swallowing with difficulty, and then felt that I would be sick if I took another scrap. Looking around at my companions, I saw that they were in the same state; in fact, Gogan was near to tears. Disconsolately we admitted defeat and stowed the wonderful dinner away in the food-locker. Thus ended what should have been an unforgettable feast. There was, however, one great consolation left to us. The good folk ashore had sent us tobacco and cigarettes. Almost reverently we each drew one from our packets. We sniffed at them, tapped them on our thumb-nails, and having lighted them, inhaled luxuriously.

Maddening that we would be leaving Fremantle before a letter from our homes could reach us. Every sailor, when his ship arrives in port, knows genuine delight when the ship's agent brings the mail on board. If ever a crew deserved letters, we did. Instead, they lay in Mollendo, thousands of miles away, awaiting our arrival. As we grumbled and groused, as sailors do in such circumstances, the steward suddenly popped his head through the doorway. "Letter for you, Paddy," and he held out an envelope towards me.

"A letter for me?" I echoed. "But how can there be any letter. . . . I mean nobody knows I'm here?"

"Well, there it is, but if you don't want it, of course . . ." and he pretended to put it in his pocket.

I snatched it from him. "Thanks, Stew." Holding the letter, I looked around at the others wondering if they had been up to some trick, unkind although it would have been, but their faces betrayed nothing but a genuine interest. I looked at the address. "*Denbigh Castle*, Fremantle, Australia." The postmark? Southsea. Southsea? My heart jumped. Had not Daisy Green told me she sometimes stayed with relatives in Southsea?

"Why don't you open the thing?" growled Charlie. It was from her! A very ordinary letter telling me that she had heard that I was missing and hoping I was well. I was thrilled yet bewildered. Apart from coming from Daisy, its value was tremendously enhanced by the fact that I was the only one on board to receive a letter. But how had she known the address? Naturally, when I met her about eighteen months later, that was one of the very first questions I asked her. She remembered writing it but could not remember addressing the envelope.

"I suppose," she said, "I knew that you were on the other side of the world somewhere, so what was more natural than to think of Australia?" That was the naïve and delightfully Daisyish explanation she gave of what, to me, is one of the most inexplicable mysteries of my life.

It was the arrival of a hamper addressed to "The apprentices of the *Denbigh Castle* from the ladies of the Mission to Seamen," that started us talking about shore leave. Gogan dived into the hamper, making a running commentary as he lifted out its contents. "Tobacco and cigarettes, now that's what I call a jolly nice present; ha! Jam! . . . and here's a box of fancy cakes . . . say, that's jolly decent of them . . . tea, butter, sugar . . . I'd like to meet these people."

"Maybe we will," said George, "I wonder what shore leave the Old Man is going to give us?"

"Yes," said Charlie, "and how much money he is going to advance us?"

"I'll go and ask Mr. Owen," I said. "It's very likely he'll know something about it."

I found him lying on his bunk, puffing away at his pipe and enjoying the first newspaper he had seen for over eight months. "Shore leave? Sorry, Paddy, but it's bad news. The Old Man passed orders a little while ago that nobody was to be allowed to go ashore."

"What, sir?" I exclaimed. "Does that mean for all the time that we are in Fremantle?"

"I'm afraid so."

"But why? If ever anyone was entitled to shore leave . . ."

"It's no use asking me, Paddy. I expect he's afraid that some of the crew, and some of you boys if it comes to that, might run away. Bad luck, but there it is."

Had I thrown a smoke bomb into the half-deck, the others could not have expressed greater shock.

"No shore leave!" they all gasped. "Well, of all the stinking, rotten tricks, this is the limit," and Gogan's head emerged from his sea-chest where he had been rummaging to see if his go-ashore clothes were at all presentable.

"There will be a queer old rumpus for'ard when the hands hear about it," said George sucking viciously at his pipe. "We have to stand for it on account of our indentures, but the crew won't." His words came true. It was eight bells at noon next day when the hands all trooped aft and mustered on the quarter-deck. They were men who felt that they had a justifiable grievance and were determined not only to have an explanation but redress.

"Old Jowl" happened to be on the poop and he glared down at them from under his shaggy eyebrows. "What do you men want?" he rumbled.

"We want to see the captain," several voices chorused. "Old Jowl" turned and hobbled below. In a couple of minutes the chart-room door suddenly opened and the Old Man stepped out on the poop. He was dressed to go ashore in a faded blue suit and a bowler hat. His face was flushed with anger as he stepped forward to the poop-rail.

"Well," he snapped, "what's your trouble now?"

On this occasion there was no hesitation among the crowd, no shuffling of feet, or looking at one another to see who was going to make a reply. Many defiant voices answered him. "What's wrong with us going ashore . . . nine months at sea . . . can't live in this ship for ever. . . ."

The captain lifted his hand. "How you expect me to hear when you all yell at the same time, I don't know, but I gather you are looking for shore leave. I passed the word to you yesterday that there isn't going to be any shore leave, and the sooner you understand it the better. Now get for'ard the lot of you."

A growl came from the men which gradually became a gabble of outrage. Suddenly Mathews stepped forward, raising his hand as a signal for the men to keep quiet. "Wait a minute, sir, you're rushing things a bit too fast. None of us has said anything about leave. What we wants is to go ashore and see the Shipping Master of this 'ere port."

For a moment Captain Evans looked nonplussed. "The Shipping Master?" he queried. "What do you want to see him for?"

"That'll be our business, sir," Mathews answered. "We 'as a right to see 'im and we demands that right." A murmur of assent arose from the men behind him.

"I am quite aware of your rights without you telling me, my man," retorted the Old Man. "Very well, if that's what you want, I'll bring him aboard to interview you this afternoon."

"That won't do, sir."

"Won't do? What do you mean 'won't do'? Are you having the impertinence to tell me what will do and what won't do aboard my own ship?"

"No, sir. I don't mean nothing like that. What I means is that you might bring off the butcher or the baker, slip him a quid and tell him to tell us that he was the Shipping Master. We wants to interview 'im in his office so as we'll know who we're talkin' to." Laughter broke out amongst the men as they realized the portent of their speaker's words, and two or three voices called out, "Good old Mat, that's the stuff!"

The Old Man's knuckles showed white on the poop-rail.

"And do you really believe," he demanded furiously, "that I am going to let you all go ashore and leave the ship derelict without a crew while you're pretending to see the Shipping Master and instead going to the nearest pub?"

"No, sir," said Mathews playing his winning card, "but there's nothing to stop say six of us goin', or even less, an' you can come with us."

"I certainly will," snapped the Old Man. "Very well, I'll make arrangements for this afternoon."

The hands were jubilant. "What did I tell yous?" squealed Kemp, "you's 'ave only to stand up for yourselves. Them fellahs aft think they're Gawdalmighty but they ain't, an' it's up to us to show 'em." Nobody troubled to shut him up. In fact, in their elation, they found his words rather gratifying. Did not the success of the morning's interview rather point to the fact that there might be a grain of truth in his policy?

In the fo'c'sle, the men harangued and argued endlessly as to those who should be chosen to see the Shipping Master. Mathews and Turner, being of an English-speaking race, were chosen automatically. Jones, Paddy and Big Charlie were also voted for but they refused. Jones said he was just putting in time to sit for a second mate's certificate and wanted a good reference from the Old Man; Paddy just shrugged his shoulders and added, "I ain't no good with that sort of talk," while Big Charlie shook his head with the comment, "I haf de good discharge for twenty-five years and I not want 'im spoiled."

"What about Froggie, 'ere?" queried Turner. "No 'arm to have France represented."

The Frenchmen's swarthy countenance lighted up with a smile. "I go, sure; I like to see what de Australian girls are like."

"If that devilish Frenchman goes, I vos go too." The angry voice of Fritz broke in.

"Devilish Frenchman? *Mon Dieu!*" and with clenched fists,

the Frenchman started elbowing his way through the others, only to be checked by restraining hands.

"Quit it, you two," growled Mathews. "This is no time for fightin'; besides, you're both on the same side, both fightin' for your rights aboard this darned ship. What say the two of them come along?" He turned to the others. "And then we'll have some peace if nothing else." The men nodded assent.

"*Bien*," beamed the Frenchman.

"Goot," and Fritz's angry features relaxed.

"'Ere," said Kemp in a shrill voice. "What's wrong wid me comin' along? I can speak hup for our rights as good as any of yer."

Big Charlie's hand closed on the scraggy shoulder. "You be a goot boy an' stop an' give de mate a hand to look after de ship." Kemp subsided. He had learnt by now to take advice from Big Charlie.

"Well, boys," said Mathews tapping out his pipe on the heel of his boot, "that's fixed. We are all agreed to ask the Shipping Master to pay off them what wants to be paid off. Our reasons are, one: this 'ere ship 'asn't been properly navigated. Two: she's been sailing without any navigatin' lights an' so endangerin' our lives. Three: the capting 'as broken 'is agreement with us in the ship's Articles by not 'avin' sufficient grub aboard for the passage so that we were nigh on starvin'. Them is three good reasons why we should want to do the 'leave her, Johnnie, leave her'. An' if those three ain't enough for him, I'm sure we can easily think up a few more. Right! We'll now call this 'ere meetin' closed."

The chosen four got a good send-off when the tug-boat *Albatross* came alongside to collect them. The crew lined the rail and cheered lustily as the tug-boat pushed off, and their deputies waved their hats jauntily in acknowledgement, all rather embarrassing for Captain Evans who rapidly disappeared into the wheel-house. Doubtless he consoled himself with the fact that the discomfiture was but momentary, for he had already interviewed the Shipping Master that morning and had given him his version of the crew's anticipated complaints.

Although Australia was perhaps more democratic than any other English-speaking country early in the century, the sympathies of the authorities ashore did not lie with the men who occupied the fo'c'sle of a sailing-ship. The Shipping Master certainly had an intimate knowledge of ships and sailors, being himself a retired master mariner. Nevertheless, it was but natural that he should be swayed, if only sub-consciously, by a captain's viewpoint. There was, alas, no Seaman's Union in those days to fight the case of the much-abused sailorman.

It was perhaps to be expected that Mathews and his three henchmen, who had left the ship with the cheers of their ship-mates ringing in their ears, returned on board in dejection, if not despair. "What's 'appened, Mat? . . . Ain't we going to be paid off? . . . 'spect the Old Man did the dirty on us. . . ." The questions were fired rapidly, eagerly, as the men clustered round.

Moodily Mathews flung his cap into his bunk. "Well, boys," he scratched his head as though uncertain how to begin, "I gave the Shipping Master all the dope as we arranged, but somehow it didn't seem to work out proper. 'Your complaints,' he says, 'arose out of matters beyond the control of your cap-ting; the 'ead winds, the bad weather, the shiftin' of the cargo . . .' Act of God, he called 'em. 'Now,' says he, 'the cargo will be retrimmed an' the ship will be certified as bein' seaworthy; you'll all be on full rations, so there's nothing to justify my allowing you to be paid off. That'll do,' he says, sharp-like when I starts to argue. 'Get back to your ship.'"

His words were received in a silence broken by Kemp.

"The whole thing is a racket fixed up between the Old Man an' 'im. Them people is always in league again' us. But all we 'as to do," and Kemp raised his right hand to emphasize his words, "all we 'as to do is to stop work. Simple, isn't it?" Another silence fell upon the men while the meaning of Kemp's words percolated into their brains, to be broken by deep chuckles from Big Charlie. "Funny, ain't it?" and Kemp whipped round towards the Finn. "Funny if yous all go to sea again in this 'ere hooker an' run short of grub an' baccy a second time. Yous'll all sit down splittin' your sides with laughter, wouldn't yous?"

"It would be more vunny if yous all get de couple of years in yail for mutiny."

"Mutiny!" Kemp wrinkled his nose and his ugly mouth twisted into a contemptuous curl. "No sailor can be 'ad up for mutiny when 'is ship is in port. She 'as to be at sea before it can be called that."

"Aye, he's right there," Mathews remarked, "but yous can be put in jail for it all the same."

Kemp laughed scornfully. "An' what if yous are put in jail? 'Aven't you been in jail for the last nine months? Aren't yous in jail now? Isn't there a better jail ashore? You gets your grub regular, an' you 'as a bed to sleep in all night, all night, mind you, no agettin' up at three in the mornin' to go up an' fight frozen canvas on a topsail yard." Kemp felt he was getting a grip of his audience now and became still more eloquent. "Listen," his voice dropped almost to a whisper, "What 'appens if we do strike? We're ataken ashore; maybe we're jailed for the night. What of it? It's free, ain't it? nofing to pay, but," and he swept a pointed finger in a semicircle embracing his listeners, "yous are brought before a court in the morning, a proper court, mind yous. No 'anky pank work like you get with the Shipping Master an the Ol' Man pumpin' a lot of lies into 'im. They gives you a lawyer to defend yous, an' if they don't, yous can employ one, see? We can put up all the evidence what Mathews told the Shipping Master this mornin'. We stands a chance of gettin' our right an' bein' paid off. Then," his voice rising in triumph, "where will the Ol' Man an' them fellahs living under the poop be then? They'll 'ave no crew, unless the Owners what did us out of our grub, likes to pay Australian wages of six poun' a month. That'll teach 'em, an we'll be the lads what teached them. The bloomin' laugh will be on us, see?"

"It would be if yous won de case," interposed Big Charlie, "but vot if yous lose it? Dere von't be any laugh den."

Kemp raised his eyebrows. "What if we lose it? They can't put us back on the ship if we refuse to work. We still 'as the laugh on the ruddy Owners an' the Ol' Man."

"Dere ain't much laugh if yous lose your pay an' be put in jail," answered Big Charlie.

"Pay?" Kemp laughed. "What pay 'as we comin' to us? Bloomin' chicken feed, that's all. If we lose, we gets fined an' put in jail for a month or so, an' then we comes out an gets a job on a sheep farm at about ten quid a month instead of three. Yous won't be long makin' up for what little yous lose in this 'ere ship, I'm telling yous." Kemp paused, and as he looked around from one face to another, a crooked grin came to his face. With the insight of an experienced orator he knew where to stop. "Well, there yous are, lads. It's up to yous," and sitting down on a sea-chest he lit a cigarette.

The hands were impressed. Undoubtedly Kemp had given them something to think about. With the memories of their late experiences still vivid in their minds, the prospect of another long passage to the west coast of South America, and a further passage around Cape Horn before arriving home to be paid off, seemed anything but inviting.

The next morning passed without incident. Stevedores came in the tug-boat *Albatross* and started trimming the patent fuel. None of us envied them their job and, incidentally, we heard that they had demanded higher wages when they discovered the discomforting effects on their skins. The hands resumed the routine of being in port, turning to at six and washing down decks, to continue after breakfast cleaning the rusty paintwork with sand and canvas preparatory to painting. The older hands made rope and wire splices and renewed portions of the running-gear. The Old Man, shaved and in his blue double-breasted suit, went ashore in the launch appointed by the agents, as he had done since our arrival. To all appearances, the normal routine of any sailing-ship lying at anchor was being carried out. To look around her decks nobody would guess that many of the crew were just biding their time to start trouble.

It blazed up shortly after noon, when the *Albatross* came alongside to take the stevedores ashore for their dinner. We had just collected our mid-day meal and brought it into the half-deck when we heard "Old Jowl" bellow, "What the hell do you think you men are doing?"

"Something's happening outside." George gulped down his last spoonful of soup. "I'll bet the men are starting trouble." Entertainment of any kind was still very scarce in the *Denbigh Castle*, and we all flocked out on deck. Ten of the hands had clambered on to the tug-boat and stood looking up at "Old Jowl" who, with his walrus moustache bristling like a porcupine's quills, glared down at them over the rail.

"We're not workin' in this hooker any more," called up Mathews. "We're goin' ashore."

"You're goin' to jail, you mean," "Old Jowl's" face became purple. "And I'll take care that the police are waiting for you when you step off that tug-boat."

"Go on, old gammy leg," jeered Kemp. "Get your porlice.

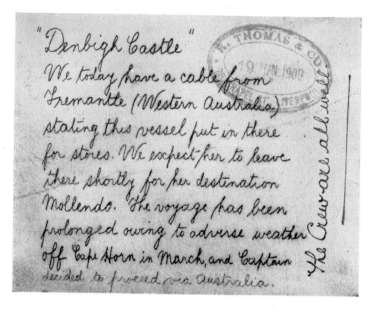

"Denbigh Castle"
We today have a cable from
Fremantle (Western Australia)
stating this vessel put in there
for stores. We expect her to leave
there shortly for her destination
Mollendo. The voyage has been
prolonged owing to adverse weather
off Cape Horn in March, and Captain
decided to proceed via Australia.

The Crew are all well

A welcome message from the owners, Messrs. Robert Thomas and
Co. of Liverpool

High Street, Fremantle, Western Australia

A magnificent picture of beauty and strength

The author in the Royal Navy
during the First World War

Captain Bestic shortly before he
retired

Call yourself a mate? You're not fit to be on a canal barge—except to lead the hoss."

The mate broke into Welsh. After his stream had subsided, he beckoned us boys. "Up on the poop an' get that police flag up," he ordered. "Lively now! I want them to meet that tug. Hold on that tug!" He roared to the master of the *Albatross*, "You're not to take those men ashore!"

The master lowered the wheel-house window and pushed his head out. "Sorry, old cock, but I'm under orders from ashore. If you want these men back, you'd better get 'em off yourself. It's none of my business." A cheer from the deck of the tug-boat led by Kemp drowned "Old Jowl's" retort. Although we lost no time in hoisting the signal, there were no police to meet the *Albatross*. It so happened that there was no necessity, for the men very wisely walked to the police station themselves and were voluntarily locked up—all except one. None of them had noticed Kemp unobtrusively detaching himself from the party. Out of loyalty to their shipmate, despised although he might be, none of the men mentioned to the police that their number was one short. Whither he went, nobody will know.

Two days passed yet there was no sign of the men returning, nor did we hear anything beyond some vague news through the cook that he thought the strikers had been sent to prison. Eagerly we scanned *The Australian Western* newspaper, kindly sent out to us by the Mission of Seamen. "Here it is!" exclaimed George, after he had turned over a couple of pages. "'Seamen from *Denbigh Castle* refuse duty!'"

"Read it out, George," said Charlie.

"Right," said George clearing his throat. "'Arising out of the refusal of a number of the crew of the ship *Denbigh Castle* to work on the vessel on Tuesday morning at Fremantle, nine seamen were presented before Messrs. Nicholis, Foxworthy and Thompson, J.P.s at the Fremantle Police Court yesterday morning charged with having on June 22nd refused to obey the lawful commands of the master of the ship.

"'Robert Evans master of the ship *Denbigh Castle*, said that the defendants were seamen on the vessel and were under a three years' contract of service which had not yet expired. Leaving Cardiff on October 9th, Staten Island off Cape Horn was sighted after 102 days out. Heavy gales were experienced which continued up to March 10th, the vessel being much buffeted about.'"

"Well, I like that!" interrupted Gogan, "buffeted about indeed! Why, we did everything but turn over! In fact, I think we did once or twice."

The reading went on, with grunts and protests interrupting.

"'The Bench, after reviewing the circumstances of the case, formally ordered each of the accused to a month's imprisonment, making a further order that the men be placed on board the vessel when she was ready to continue her voyage. Turner and Mathews, as principals in the affair, were each in addition fined 12 days' pay. Captain Evans expects that the *Denbigh Castle* will be ready to resume her voyage before Saturday next.'"

"Well, there you are," said George, "that's the lot."

Came the day when we were due to sail on the morrow. "I suppose," Gogan remarked, "we'll be seeing the jail-birds any hour now."

"Very likely they are on their way at this moment," I answered. "It's just eleven o'clock, and the *Albatross* has pushed off from the quay. I bet the men are aboard her. I only hope they'll get some dinner."

At about six bells, I had happened to glance into the galley when passing and seen the cook lolling on his bench in front of the fire apparently asleep. Considering it unwise to waken him, on the principle, "let sleeping dogs lie," I told the others.

"The blighter may be ill," commented George. "Perhaps I'd better tell Mr. Owen. Nice state of affairs if we have to go without our dinner; besides, Cookie wouldn't use his chopper on an officer."

Mr. Owen, when he heard the news, stepped into the galley and gave the cook a shake. "Hey, Cook, wake up! What's the matter with you?" Our chef opened a bleary eye, gave a reconciliatory smile and then subsided again. "Hey, Cook, snap out of it." Impatiently, the second mate gave him a more violent shake.

The cook sat up. "Well, if it isn't Misser Owen," his speech was definitely blurred. "Listen, Misser Owen. When two Welshmen get together, what do they do? They sing, Misser Owen. You're a Weshman, I'm a Weshman, and so, look you, we'll sing. One, two, three," and in a wavering cracked voice, Cookie began a Welsh hymn, at the same time conducting with his hand.

"You're drunk, you old fool! Where did you get the stuff?"

The cook put his forefinger on one side of his nose and leered cunningly up at the second mate. "Sorry I can't offer you a li'l drink, Mr. Owen, 'cos you're a decent man . . . wish is more than I can say for some of the others, look you."

Mr. Owen wisely realized that it was no use losing his temper. "Look here, Cook, it's just six bells, only one hour off dinner. The hands are coming back and there'll be the devil to pay if you've no grub ready, see? Pull yourself together and get going. What's more, if the Old Man hears about it, he'll dock three days' pay off you."

"Al'right, Mr. Owen, you're a fine felleh, so I'll get the dinner for you. I've cooked dinners for hundreds and hundreds in me day, an' it won't take me long to dish up a bit of stuff for a few sailors; no trouble whatever."

"Fair enough, then, you get crackin'." Mr. Owen stepped out of the galley and nodded towards us. "You boys keep an eye on him and let me know if he falls asleep again." Just then, a hoot came from the whistle of the *Albatross* as she made a semicircle preparatory to coming alongside, and we ran across the deck to take her mooring-lines. As she came to a stop with a kick astern of her engines, our old shipmates clambered on board. They appeared to be in the best of spirits.

"Hallo, Paddy," Turner said to me with a joviality which I guessed to be partly alcoholic, "how are things?"

"Fine," I replied. "Thought you chaps weren't going to come back to the ship any more?"

Turner winked. "Don't tell anybody, son, but we hasn't come back for good, not by a long chalk. The bloke in the jail says, 'your ship is sailin' tomorrow, so you chaps are being put aboard 'er today.' At first we was goin' to refuse, an' then Mathews says, 'what's wrong with goin' aboard an' 'aving our dinner an' gettin' a bit of fresh air, just for a bit of change like, then we can go on strike again an' finish our month.' So 'ere we are. Funny, ain't it? But don't you go an' tell any of the officers, mind."

"That's all right," I answered. "All said an' done, it's their business not mine."

"Sure," and he gave me a pat on the shoulder and went for'ard after the others.

If the men had come on board in order to get a good meal after their prison fare, they had chosen the wrong day. Although we had been keeping our eye on the galley, Cookie's efforts were a complete failure. The soup was a mixture of cabbage water and boiled-down grease. The potatoes could not have been boiled for longer than about three minutes, if indeed they had been boiled at all, and the meat was raw. Suddenly, as we sat in the half-deck glumly surveying this mess, we heard yells and curses coming apparently from the galley, interposed with cries for help!

"That's the cook in trouble or I'm a Dutchman!" exclaimed George. Cookie certainly was in trouble. Furious at the ruin of their dinner, the men had come aft in a body. One had scrambled up on top of the galley and, having opened the galley skylight, had emptied the big saucepan of so-called soup over the luckless water-spoiler. Simultaneously, the hands had gathered at each galley door armed with the hard potatoes, and were bombarding the cook from both sides at once. Their aim was proved by yells from the target. If the cook had been drunk before, he now went completely berserk. The bombardment finally ceasing owing to the ammunition having run out, he grasped his meat-chopper and emerged through the galley door, a weird and terrible figure. Soup streamed down from his hair and straggly beard on to his clothes. His eyes flashed with a wild fire, and the chopper was raised above his head ready to cleave the first head which might come within his reach, while curses in Welsh and English spat from his mouth.

Instinctively, like leaves before a sudden and violent gust of wind, the men scattered, jostling one another in their efforts to escape. Some actually sprang for the rigging while the others sprinted for'ard. Just as the cook threw back his arm to hurl the chopper at the fleeing figures rather than lose his revenge, his feet slipped in the dripping grease and he sat down unexpectedly on the deck. That seemed to bring him to his senses and he got to his feet. For a moment he stood there looking around him dazedly, his gaunt figure drooping pathetically. Then, picking up his chopper, he shambled into his galley.

Our precious dinner-hour always seemed to pass over too quickly and, as I browsed over a newspaper contentedly smoking my pipe, Charlie dug me in the ribs. "One o'clock," he reminded me, "you're on the bells." With a sigh I went up on the poop and rang two bells. "Old Jowl's" stiff leg appeared over the chart-room step. Advancing to the break of the poop he removed the clay pipe from his mouth and produced his whistle. "Hands turn to!" Once more we apprentices renewed our monotonous job of removing the rust from the bulwarks of the *Denbigh Castle*. Big Charlie, Paddy, Taff Jones and some of the others emerged from the fo'c'sle doors and got on with their jobs. Of the "mutineers", as we sometimes called them, there was no sign. Down the poop ladder, one step at a time, "Old Jowl" clumped for'ard.

"Come along, you men; turn to!" he bellowed. "You're not resting in jail now!" There was no response; save from the seagulls protesting raucously.

A few seconds later, Turner and Mathews, followed by the others, stepped out through the fo'c'sle door. They were dressed in their go-ashore clothes and carried sea-bags. "Old Jowl" glared at them in astonishment. "And what do you fellows think you are playin' at?" he demanded.

"This ain't no play, Mister," Mathews replied insolently. "It just means that we're fed up with you an' this ship. You can hoist your bloomin' police flag. We're goin' back to jail."

Once more we went through the routine of hoisting the police flag. This was the second occasion which the signal had been made from the *Denbigh Castle* since she had arrived in Fremantle and, when the police arrived in their launch, they came in force. They were undoubtedly surprised and somewhat disconcerted when they saw a crowd of men leaning over the rail, waving their caps and welcoming them with a cheer.

"Welcome on board, Cookie," said Turner as the sergeant climbed on deck. "We wants you to take us back to that nice little hotel of yours."

Ignoring him, the sergeant marched up to the break of the poop and looked up at "Old Jowl" who, leaning on the rail with arms folded and his clay pipe in his mouth, contemplated the scene with apparent indifference. "What's the trouble, Mr. Mate?" he demanded.

"Old Jowl" removed his pipe, spat dexterously over the rail, and nodded towards the hands. "You can take 'em away from here; they refuse to work and so they're no good to me. I wouldn't take any chances with them, if I were you; some of 'em are dangerous . . . better put the bracelets on 'em."

"Right you are, Mr. Mate. Put the handcuffs on them, boys. Here, you," and he turned to Mathews, "let's see your wrists."

"'Ere, what's this for?" demanded Mathews. "It was us that sent for yeh, yeh fool! We *want* to go to jail."

"That's all right, you're goin' there, don't you worry. Come on, hold 'em out." Reluctantly Mathews and the rest obeyed, and thus secured, they were helped over the rail into the launch. From where I stood I could see a twinkle in the mate's eye, and I am sure his big moustache concealed a grin.

We never saw those men again. I watched the launch becoming smaller, as it chugged shorewards. I knew them all, for had I not lived, worked and almost died with them? It seemed unjust that such men should be imprisoned. They were children of the sea and prison was no place for them.

Undoubtedly the voyage up to the present had been an extremely unlucky one for Captain Evans. Already the expenses incurred by the unusually long passage must have far exceeded the return for the freightage. Now, owing to the latest action of the crew, the vessel would be further delayed in port, and new men would demand a higher wage.

As mate of the ship, "Old Jowl" had to replace the missing men, a job not to his liking. The usual procedure for a mate, when crews could not be obtained from a shipping-office, was to visit the local dockside taverns, dish drinks out all round, and try to convey that a crew under his charge would be the happiest company afloat. The captain would be depicted as a sort of father confessor who adopted those under him as though they were his children, and issued a glass of grog whenever there was a shower of rain. The ship had to be praised for her wonderful sailing-qualities and for possessing such phenomenal luck that head-winds were almost unheard of. Since the local reporters had reported all the details concerning the *Denbigh Castle*, "Old Jowl" realized that orthodox propaganda methods could only meet with failure. He would have to offer very attractive wages.

The steward was in his pantry having a quiet read and smoke when he heard "Old Jowl" clumping down the companion-stairs and entering the saloon where the captain sat. Unobtrusively the steward laid aside his paper and opened the pantry door another inch to ensure that he did not miss any conversation.

The Old Man looked up from the list of ship's expenses which he was preparing for the Owners. "Evenin', Mr. Evans."

"Evenin', sir. I just dropped in to ask you about these new men we have to find."

"Aye, and what about them? Sit down."

With a grunt, the mate lowered himself into one of the swivel-chairs and manœuvred his gammy leg out in front of him. "From all accounts, men are scarce ashore and, so far as I can see, the only way to get 'em is to offer 'em good wages."

"Naturally, we'll have to offer whatever wages are being paid on the Australian coast."

"Old Jowl" shook his head dubiously. "I reckon we'll have to pay 'em a pound a month above that."

"A pound?" The captain frowned and tapped the end of his pencil on the table. "The accounts here," and he flicked the papers on the table before him, "for wages, Agent's fees, trimming cargo, extra provisions and what not are going to make the Owners fall off their stools when they get them. What'll happen when they hear they have to pay Australian wages and more, I'm sure I don't know."

"Old Jowl" had a very good idea what would happen but he was not going to tell his captain. In all probability he would get the sack, Australian wages or no. Instead, he grunted sympathetically and then returned to the matter in hand. "Reckon, sir, we won't get anyone to sign on for under five pound. They know ashore that the ship must sail, an' they also know she can't sail without a crew."

This time Captain Evans flung his pencil angrily on the table. "Of all the unlucky voyages I ever made, this one beats the lot From the day we sailed, it's been one trouble after another. Oh, well," he added resignedly, "do your best, Mr. Mate. I expect I'll get the sack in any case, so what's the odds? You'd better go ashore now."

The mate rolled the tobacco he had pared and began thrusting it into his pipe. "I suppose, sir, a fiver should do to go on with."

"Oh, you want an advance of a fiver, do you? Going to buy yourself a new rig-out?" queried the Old Man facetiously.

"Advance? I want no advance." A twinkle showed in "Old Jowl's" eyes. "It's for bait."

"Bait?"

"Yes, sir, for drinks to catch the new hands with."

The Old Man grunted irritably as he raked his pocket for the keys of the safe.

CHAPTER NINE

NEW HANDS

ONCE again the *Denbigh Castle* was at sea, dipping and swaying to tumbling wintry seas. We were back again to the familiar scenes of water and sky. Once again a man was standing beside the revolving spokes of the wheel, and "Old Jowl", in long oilskin coat and sou'wester, was balancing himself under the lee of the poop-dodger, occasionally clutching at the gaff-stay when the vessel gave a heavy roll.

The Old Man had replenished the slop-chest, and we now possessed warm underwear, new oilskins and sea-boots. The food, too, was of a better quality than we had when we left Cardiff, especially in the matter of salt beef and biscuits. More important, perhaps, our ship was again seaworthy. No longer did we experience that dreadful sensation that, after she gave a heavy roll to leeward, she might not come back.

After rounding Cape Leeward, at the sou'-west corner of Australia, she rushed foaming to the eastward, as though with a renewed purpose before the freshening winds. Her pride in her appearance had been restored to a great extent. Gone was the depressing green coating of seaweed from the decks, thanks to our vigorous scrubbing with new brooms. The bulwarks and paintwork, too, now cleaned from rust and given a couple of coats of white paint not only helped to renew her self-respect but was pleasing to the eye.

"Old Jowl's" efforts had not been without success. The captain, sore, no doubt, because nobody would sign on the articles for less than five pounds said that the men would have to be discharged when the ship reached Mollendo.

The steward, when visiting the cook in the galley during the second dog-watch, recalled the interview. ". . . An' I nigh split me sides laughin', tryin' to keep it choked up like, with me in the pantry, when I heard the two of 'em. 'Old Jowl' comes puffin' an' blowin' down the companion-way into the saloon after he comes on board with his new recruits, an' the Old Man, he says, 'Well, Mister Mate, did yeh have any luck?'

"'Old Jowl', he just nods. 'I've made up the number all right, sir, but as I told you, the wages is five poun'.'

"The Old Man does a tch-tch-tch, an' then he says, 'I suppose we're lucky to get sailors at all.'

"'Sailors?' says 'Old Jowl', 'there ain't no sailors in Fremantle. Three of the fellahs I've got are fishermen, four of 'em are off a sheep farm, an' the other two keep chickens.'

"Lor' save us, yeh should have seen the Old Man! I never saw 'im take on so. 'Snakes alive!' an' he jumps to his feet. 'Five poun' for sheep farmers an' chicken killers? What do you think this ship is? A floatin' hen-house?'

"'Old Jowl', he don't turn a hair. 'They'll turn out all right, sir. They're young an' keen, an' I'll soon make sailors of 'em. I've made good men out of a darned sight worse material in me time,' and with that he turns on 'is 'eel an' walks into his cabin. The Ol' Man got no change out of him."

"Old Jowl" had made no delay in starting his training. A dozen times in a watch he had the newcomers up aloft overhauling bunt-lines, reeving new rovings, making up gaskets that had come adrift besides many other little jobs which are always in demand from the sails of a sailing-ship. On the very first day out to sea, one man, Harry Stevens, nearly took unintentional revenge on "Old Jowl" by being sick from the crossjack-yard, but the mate stepped nimbly aside in time, and unsympathetically made Harry clean up the mess with a bucket and broom as soon as he descended.

Like the parable concerning the labourers in the vineyard, the new arrivals caused a certain amont of dissension on board. Here were unskilled men receiving five pounds per month whereas those men who had qualified to become able seamen by spending three gruelling years at sea, were only receiving three pounds. Further, when sail had to be taken in which under ordinary conditions could be carried out by one watch, it was a case of calling all hands on deck. We boys in the half-deck felt we had a still greater grievance. When the Fremantle men were sent up aloft to do odd jobs, one of us boys had also to go with them to show how the work should be done.

"It's a shame," and Gogan stepped into the half-deck and shook snow off his oilskins. "Here am I getting four pounds a year paid back to me out of a premium, and I have to teach these five pounds a month hoboes their job."

"It seems all wrong to me," I answered gloomily, having had to spend a considerable amount of my time up aloft on a similar mission. "The trouble is there's nothing we can do about it."

"We could go and complain to the Old Man." We all turned and looked at George in astonishment.

"A jolly good idea," Charlie commented.

"Yes, but . . ." I hesitated, "who's going to do the interviewing?" My mind had disturbing visions that lots might be drawn and, as I was usually unlucky, it might fall upon me.

"We could all go," said George.

"A splendid idea," I exclaimed enthusiastically before anybody had time to propose something different. "There's no time like the present."

"Come on." George laid the wheezy pipe on the little shelf

above his bunk, and we followed him through the doorway. The steward having been instructed to ask the Old Man if he would give us an interview, and the request having been granted, we assembled, caps in hand, before the August Presence in the saloon.

The captain did not look up from the book he was reading for nearly a minute. Eventually he glanced at us over the tops of his spectacles and snapped out, "Well?"

There was a momentary silence, and then George bravely took a step forward. "It's like this, sir . . ." he began.

"What's like what?"

"We were wondering, sir," continued George stoutly, "if we could have some sort of compensation."

"Compensation? What for?"

"For the extra work, sir. The crew on board, sir, don't know their job and we have to teach them."

"So that's what's biting you, is it?" The Old Man kept nodding his head slowly as though gradually absorbing the information. "You have to teach the new men their job. Do you know," and he leaned forward and placed his closed fist heavily on the table, "that if I was a boy in your place I'd be proud to be able to pass on my knowledge to others, and my ability to do so would more than compensate me for any little trouble it might involve."

As George seemed somewhat nonplussed, Charlie stepped into the breach. "Of course we are glad to be able to help in any way, sir, but our point is that it means a lot of extra work which we would not have had were these men able seamen, the same as we shipped at Cardiff. So we thought that perhaps you might give us a little extra money, sir." Good old Charlie, I thought; now what will the Old Man have to say to that?

I watched him, and was disappointed to see that he did not seem the least perturbed. He settled himself more comfortably in his chair and crossed his legs. "Tell me, did you boys read over your indentures before you signed them?"

"Yes, sir," we all murmured.

"Very well. Did you not notice a clause which stated that the undersigned apprentice promises to remain loyal to his captain and officers and," he leaned forward and tapped the edge of the table with the palm of his hand, "that he will uphold the interests of the Company in every way—in every way, mark you?" He paused, and as we did not reply, took our silence for consent. "Yet here you are, not a dog-watch at sea, with the ink from your signatures scarcely dry, asking me for money. Not only are you dishonouring your own signatures but you are letting down the signatures of your parents or whoever signed in their place. By instructing these men as best you can and so helping the ship, you are but doing your duty." He paused, waiting for one of us to reply but we had nothing to say.

Our dreams of extra wealth—mine had not risen above ten shillings a month—had been dispelled by the Old Man's cleverness in finding the one weak point in our claim, and with his nod of dismissal we filed up the companion-way and returned to the half-deck. As we sat down moodily on our sea-chests Gogan was the first to break the silence. "I think," and his features broke into a grin, "that the only thing to do when we get to Mollendo is go to jail."

The days passed and the course made by the *Denbigh Castle* gradually took her down to the now familiar latitudes of the Roaring Forties. It was mid-winter. Angry snow-laden clouds, driven before the ever-freshening winds, raced up from astern and swept low over her reeling mast-heads. Frequently, flakes would come flying, darting and whisking in bewildering fashion, and the vessel, covered in a white mantle, would suddenly become transformed into a ghostly outline swinging dizzily through some strange world of unreality. Black seas with foaming caps rushed at her out of the murk and, speeding for'ard on each side of the hull, tumbled several tons of water on board.

More frequently too came the whistle from one of the mates followed by the call, "All hands on deck!" Seldom did we remove our clothes in our watch below but lay on our bunks watching our smoking oil-lamp, which hung from the deck-head, describing dizzy circles. If we fell asleep it was a sleep of exhaustion after struggling with a kicking topsail which, through lack of skilled handling, refused to be secured. "And to think," said Gogan, after we had been battling up aloft in our watch below for three hours, "of those mutineers sleeping throughout the whole night in their cosy little cells with warders to attend on them. What fools we are!"

In one sense we were fortunate that we still had some good men left on board. Big Charlie, Old Paddy, Taffy Jones, besides seven other able seamen, had refused to join the strikers. Fortunately, too, the new men were, literally, getting to know the ropes, and eager to tackle any job. Taking in sail on a dark night when the ship is rolling, however, is a job for professional seamen, and there was always an anxiety on such occasions that one of the newcomers might lose his foothold.

As the *Denbigh Castle* tumbled and reeled her way along the base of the Great Australian Bight, we speculated on whether the Old Man would choose to go through Bass Strait, between Tasmania Island and the mainland, or make a course to the southward.

"I'll gamble on the Straits." Gogan was poring over a school atlas he had brought with him from home, and which he called his "charts".

"On what grounds, Mister Navigator?" said Charlie, who was lying on his bunk, propping himself up on his elbow.

"Well, in the first place, it's ever so much shorter. Why, you cut off miles and miles."

"That may be so," and George looked over Gogan's shoulder at the map, "but you've far less sea-room. Also there are rocks here and there, which an Australian once told me are very hard."

"There's another point," I chipped in. "If you go south of Tasmania you are down in latitude forty-five, and if you ask me anything, the higher the latitude the less the Old Man likes it. The weather is sticky enough here at forty."

"There's some truth in that all right," George commented. "But he also likes plenty of sea-room."

"Supposing," I queried, "the wind whipped around ahead just after we'd entered the Strait? What then?"

"We'd have to sail out again, I suppose," George pointed to the map with his pipe-stem, "and sail down here to the south'ard. We couldn't tack to and fro in the Strait."

"If you ask me anything," Charlie's head bobbed up from his pillow again, "the Old Man will be guided by the weather. If it looks as though it is going to keep clear, no heavy snow falls and all that, he'll tackle the Strait, but it wouldn't be nice going through there without seeing any landmarks." Charlie's deduction was obviously right.

It so happened that on the day we sighted Tasmania the weather was fine and clear, and the ship was running before a fresh to strong wind. The decision had to be made without further delay, otherwise it would mean having to sail down the west coast of Tasmania on a lee shore a little too close for comfort. I happened to be at the wheel that morning and saw the captain and "Old Jowl" conferring together on the poop. Presently the Old Man came aft and, glancing into the binnacle, said, "Port two points."

"Port two points, sir," I answered gladly. It meant that the ship's course was being altered to pass through the Strait. At the same time "Old Jowl's" whistle rang out. "Lee fore brace!" As the wind came around on to the port quarter, the yards were canted into the best position to keep the sails full. The *Denbigh Castle* increased her speed, for now instead of the sails on the fore- and main-masts being blanketed by the sails on the mizzen while the wind was aft, every sail was filled. The ship herself seemed to reflect our mood, for everybody wanted to take the short cut. The seas roared and tumbled up under her weather quarter, lifted her stern with a canting roll and then raced for'ard. As a swell came under her bow, the vessel would pause slightly, to resume her headlong rush as she was carried along by the next sea.

Our triumph, alas, was short-lived. As we approached the entrance to the Strait, the weather suddenly changed. Black clouds appeared from nowhere, the blue sky was obliterated, and the dancing sparkle of the foam-capped seas disappeared to be replaced by a leaden sea curling in sullen whiteness before the rising wind. Suddenly, as though the cauldron of hell was opened, the storm broke like an avenging terror. It came with a vibrating roar which warned of a frightening strength. Above it could be heard sobs and shrieks, as though tortured demons were crying out in anguish. Next instant the ship was enveloped in whirling snow, tearing, darting, racing madly with the speed of the tormented atmosphere. Visibility vanished. From the poop the fo'c'sle head showed up as a shadowy outline, and beyond it, nothing. Under straining lower t'gallant sails, the ship sped like a hunted stag. The extra hand called to the wheel could do little to prevent her yawing wildly when the crest of each sea came amidships . . . and how important it was that she should maintain a steady course in these narrow waters.

Nobody was taken by surprise at the call of "All hands on deck". Our only hope was to reduce sail and heave the vessel to, until visibility became clear. Encouraged by the older hands the men, to the sound of the traditional weird cries and yells, hauled lustily on the bunt-lines and clew-lines. Imperturbable as ever, "Old Jowl" clumped his way around the deck slacking away the sheets and bellowing orders. We tackled the mizzen t'gallant sail first and, presently, as the bunt-lines pulled the foot of the sail up to the yard, the sail assumed the appearance of big swaying balloons straining to be released.

"Up aloft and stow!" We dragged ourselves upwards into the whirling void, our numb fingers clutching the stays. We clung like flies on reaching the top, where the rigging cants outwards, waiting for the counter-roll when, with bodies momentarily vertical, we continued to climb. We struggled out along the yard with feet sliding upon the ice-covered foot-rope. It seemed as though we had been transported into a strange world whose inhabitants must breathe snow instead of air. "Old Jowl", the decks, even the ship herself was lost to sight. The yard to which we clung seemed to be something apart, as though we had drifted into space, carried off by the big angry balloons with which we had now to do battle.

Big Charlie yelled out something, but with such a howling wind few of us heard him. Above us a wire, known as a yard-lift, came slantwise from the mast to the yard-arm, and suddenly Big Charlie was standing upright on the yard itself, holding himself in position by this lift. Next instant he had stepped on to the sail. We clutched desperately at the ridge created in the canvas by his weight and, with a wild yell, dragged it home. Again and again we repeated this process. We fought each balloon with a strength made superhuman by frenzied anger and the knowledge that we had to remain on the yard until the sail was conquered.

We overcame six big sails in succession and then, with but

three lower topsails set, braced the yards upon the starboard tack ready to heave-to. "All hands lay aft on the poop!" The words seemed to penetrate vaguely into my brain as I staggered aft with the others. I had no hands or feet, and if I had, they were out of control. Black patches floated across my eyes, momemtarily blinding me. As I clambered up the ladder, the snow-covered poop gave me the impression that I was aboard a ghost ship. To add to the illusion, the white figures of the captain, "Old Jowl" and the man at the wheel kept disappearing and reappearing. An overwhelming longing came over me to lie down. To lie down on the Olympian heights of the poop? In fear I fought against the temptation. They might even think I was trying to shirk work. Paddy, the shirker. Although the numbness of my fingers and toes seemed to have penetrated my whole body, I kept on my feet. Up aloft, except for my extremities, I had been sweating beneath my oilskins. Now the chilled perspiration seemed to make me feel colder.

As I reached a position by the mizzen-mast and clung to the iron belaying-pins attached to it, I felt that the motion of the ship had changed and that she was now rolling very heavily. Vaguely I realized that the helm must have been put down and that she was describing a semicircle so as to bring the wind round on to the bow. Suddenly the belaying-pins which I was holding seemed to disappear and I felt myself sliding. A hand clutched my arm and a distant voice said, "Steady up, son." Blackness came once more but I felt a rope being passed around my body. "Here! What the . . .!" I recognized the face of my old friend, Paddy, close to mine.

"You nearly took a dip that time, young feller-me-lad," he remarked, grinning. "You keep that line around you until she comes up into the wind." I nodded, and once more clung to the belaying-pins. Presently I felt the excessive rolling ease off and I knew the ship must be hove-to.

A faint cheer unexpectedly came from the hands. Stupid fools, I thought; what can anybody find to cheer about? It only added to my feeling of unreality. A sharp dig in the ribs made me look around. "It's grog-o!" Paddy's face, although salt-begrimed and unshaven, looked positively gleeful.

"Oh, is that all?" I answered disinterestedly. For me the words had no meaning; I had never even tasted rum. I had heard the men talking about it being issued aboard ships in which they had previously served, and that was all.

"'Ere, get it down the hatch." Paddy was standing in front of me holding an enamel mug under my nostrils. It smelt abominably.

I shook my head. "You take it, Paddy; the smell of the beastly stuff is enough for me. It would make me sick."

"Drink it, do yer hear, or I'll dot you one on the kisser!" Then his manner changed. "Now son, would I ever tell you anything that wasn't for your own good? Don't you remember the time I made ye chew a piece of baccy? Drink this up, there's a good lad." Reluctantly I took the mug from him and raised it to my lips. I was mildly surprised to hear it rattling against my teeth. I tilted it back farther and the liquid ran down my throat. Next instant I was coughing and spluttering. Surely I was going to choke? Alarmed, Paddy grabbed the mug out of my hand, afraid that I might spill the precious contents.

I looked at him through my streaming eyes. Already I felt the fiery liquid coursing through my veins. My dizziness vanished. I smiled at the old sailor and held out my hand. "I'll finish that."

Paddy grinned and wiped his nose with the back of his hand. "Good lad," and he handed me back the mug.

"That'll do the watch!" bellowed "Old Jowl". I laughed, not caring had he said, "Take in the lower topsails."

It was my watch below and, as I opened the half-deck door, the warm air from our little bogie stove greeted me like a breath from heaven. My shipmates had forestalled me and, though still in their oilskins, were removing their sea-boots before lying down on their bunks.

"I must say," said Charlie, turning his sea-boot down to empty out the water, "that it's a long time since I put in six hours like that. I'm about all in."

"All in?" I exclaimed, glad to learn that somebody else had felt the strain. "Why, if it hadn't been for that sup of grog I would have been all out!"

"Grog?" Charlie echoed in amazement. "Did you say you got some grog? Why, I lined up with the rest of the hands when it was being issued, and the Old Man said it was against the rules for apprentices to get any. How did you get it?"

Suddenly the truth dawned on me. Old Paddy must have given me a portion of his allowance!

"Paddy gave me some of his," I answered rather shame-facedly. Then, laying my head on my pillow, I immediately fell asleep.

"All hands on deck!" Startled, I lifted my head and glanced at our little alarm clock swinging dizzily from its cuphook screwed into the deckhead. Three o'clock in the afternoon and we had turned in at two, so it was still my watch below. How could it be all hands on deck when the ship was snugged down and hove-to? I glanced around at my companions, none of whom was moving. Must have been dreaming, I thought, and let my head sink back on the pillow.

Next instant the half-deck door was flung open admitting a blast of icy cold air. "Now then, now then!" It was the voice of Mr. Owen. "All hands on deck. Look lively, lads! Out of those bunks right away." This was no dream. Legs swung out over bunks, and tousled heads, eyes bleary with sleep, were lifted from pillows. Soon George stood by the half-deck door. "Ready, boys?" We nodded and followed him out on deck.

Blessed relief, the snow had ceased, although it was still blowing hard with a high sea running. These seas were dangerous and more steep than the mighty grey-beards off Cape Horn. The distance also from crest to crest was shorter, thus giving the ship less opportunity to recover when she sank into the valleys.

"Old Jowl" was on the poop with the captain and he motioned us to go for'ard. "Give them a hand with those head sails!" he yelled. Head sails? I ducked and dodged for'ard with the others. Why do they want to set three little fore-and-aft sails on the bowsprit when the ship is hove-to? And why all hands on deck when one watch could do it easily? As we clambered up the fo'c'sle-head ladder, we found Mr. Owen in charge of operations. Four hands were out on the swaying and dipping bowsprit casting off the gaskets which held the sail secured. Others held the halliards ready to hoist away directly the sails were freed. I spotted Paddy in the group and sidled up eager for news. "What's in the wind, Paddy?"

"Did ye not see what's to leeward?" and he jerked his thumb in the direction of the port quarter. I looked over the tumbling waste of water waiting for the bows to rise so that I could have a good view of the horizon. Suddenly, about a mile away, a huge column of water and spray shot into the air as though forced upwards by a submarine explosion.

"Good Lord!" I exclaimed. "What's that?"

"Them is the Crocodile Rocks. A good name for them too. If they get their teeth into this ship she won't last very long. Lucky for us the snow cleared off fifteen minutes ago."

"And what's happening now?"

"Well, directly the Old Man spotted the rocks, he ordered 'up helm' so that the ship would pay off an' bring the wind astern, but the cranky old girl refused to budge. So now we're settin' these head sails so that the wind can exert more pressure to push her bow round, see? If she won't pay off, she'll just drift sideways on to the rocks."

As Paddy had pointed out, with the wind on the starboard bow, we were making no headway. The ship therefore would have to be turned in a half-circle to allow the wind to come behind her. Unfortunately, the turn would have to be made to port in the direction of the rocks. Would she turn in a small enough circle to clear them?

"Haul away inner jib halliards!" Mr. Owen's shout interrupted my speculations, and balancing ourselves as best we could on the swinging and heaving fo'c'sle head, we obeyed. The hanks travelled up the stay, and the sail flapped with a sound like a cowboy's whip. Still higher it rose and we anticipated that, after another three hauls or so, Mr. Owen would call out "belay". The halliards of this sail were never belayed. With unexpected suddenness a squall shrieked across the waters, struck the ship, wrenched the sail from its fastenings, whisked it up in the air and then hurled it to leeward like a pocket-handkerchief. Stupidly, reprovingly, we stood gazing as it darted and twisted rapidly into space. It had no right to do that, no right to flaunt all our energy in hoisting it.

"Outer jib halliards, men; come on, jump to it!" shouted Mr. Owen. We forced the outer jib up its stay, giving that extra little kick into our hauling which anxiety can always produce. Halliards and sheet secured, we tackled the flying jib, situated at the extreme end of the bowsprits, and set it without further mishap. A buffalo roar from "Old Jowl" floated up to us against the wind. "Hands lay aft on the poop!"

"Lively now, lively," urged Mr. Owen. "The decks will be full up directly." We needed no urging. In little short sprints when the deck became level, pausing to grab a life-line here, a fife-rail there, running with bodies balanced at an angle to the deck, we all reached the poop. Suddenly I saw the steward emerging from the companionway clutching an armful of life-jackets. It was far more significant than the spoken word.

The inaction increased the tension. All that could be done had been done. The ship herself must decide our fate, and her own. At length, as though against her will, she began to move. Her bow slid into a steep valley and the next sea, swinging her bow skywards, flung her off a full point.

"She's moving, Captain!" The shout from "Old Jowl" who, imperturbable as ever, was standing with legs stretched apart in front of the compass, was heard by us all. Once the initial movement began, enabling her to make headway as the wind gained more power behind the sails, she could feel the effect of her rudder. Presently the wind and sea came abeam and she was racing, as it appeared to us, towards her doom. Her gaunt masts tore wildly across the sky as though appealing for help. Angry seas with sides as steep as a cliff hurled themselves against her hull and, with a triumphant roar, swept madly across her reeling decks. At times, with nothing visible except the fo'c'sle head and the tops of the deck-houses, she paused, wallowing helplessly at being over-burdened with so much weight of water. Still swinging, she brought the ascending column of water and spray almost ahead. They were close now, so close that we could see their black fangs showing momentarily in the fall of the seas.

"Another hand to the wheel!" The wind was well on the quarter now and the rocks were just forward of the beam, so close that we could hear the thunderous roaring of the surf. They seemed to rush towards us to come abeam, and it looked as though we were separated from them by about three seas. A few seconds later and they were on our quarter—and receding rapidly aft. We looked at each other, and I felt a strange inclination to shake hands with somebody. Sheepishly we took off our life-jackets, as though ashamed of having ever put them on.

"Square away cro' jack-yards!" Ordinary ship routine again, with "Old Jowl" there to give orders, braces to be hauled upon, yards to be trimmed, the captain still on the poop and the helmsman at the wheel. Eagerly we plunged into the water on the main deck and pulled with a will. A ray of feeble sunshine burst through the driving clouds like a benediction, and the *Denbigh Castle* continued her passage through the Strait.

CHAPTER TEN

RESCUE

IT was now over four months since the *Denbigh Castle* had left Fremantle. Her ordeal in Bass Strait was a distant memory to those of us on board, if indeed it was remembered at all. The ship moved easily through the waters of the Pacific with all sail set, the centre of an immense solitude of sea and sky.

Once more we boys started probing the cook for galley news, but he professed no knowledge of our position "whatever". I happened to be on top of the galley close to the skylight painting the lifeboat when the steward entered to collect the dinner for the cabin. "I've been in a few ships in my time," he remarked irritably, "but I never heard the likes of it before."

"What is it that troubles you now, man?"

"The Old Man an' the mates, they don't know where we are."

"Not know where we are?" There was surprise in the cook's tone. "Indeed and to goodness I never heard the likes of that, look you."

"Well, it's a fact. I heard the Old Man tell the mate that the chronometers must have gone haywire because when he took a sight by the sun, it showed the ship's position to be on top of the Andes. Nice place to finish up the passage after being over a year out from Cardiff, I must say."

"We must have signed on a Noah's ark, look you," and chuckling, the cook turned to his pots and pans. It was stop-press news, and I relished the stir it created amongst my companions when I announced it a few minutes later at dinner.

"At the top of the Andes?" exclaimed Gogan. He stopped eating and, with knife and fork poised upwards, gazed at me. "Good Lord! Where is this bally ship going to take us next, I wonder?"

"Is this one of your funny yarns?" queried Charlie.

I shook my head. "It's no yarn of mine. Perhaps the steward was pulling Cookie's leg."

"The steward hasn't got the brains to think that one up," remarked George.

"It seems strange," mumbled Charlie, his mouth half-full, "but it looks as though the Old Man forgot to wind the chronometers some morning or other. That would upset their daily rate."

Gogan started peeling another potato. "More likely he made a botch of it when he was taking a sight, or perhaps working it out."

"But he always takes about three sights," I pointed out. "He would hardly make a botch of the whole three. Besides, he's working them out every day. It's not like us who only try to work one out every two months or so."

"I've never got one quite right yet," sighed Gogan reaching for another potato. "I only hope they'll be able to teach me something in the Navigation School, that's all."

"You'd better become a steward instead of an executive officer," commented George. "You'd be a darned sight handier with a knife and fork than a sextant."

Suddenly we heard a cry, "LAND-HO!" and, with one accord, sprang to our feet. Next instant we were all out on deck. I gazed at the horizon ahead but, to my utter disappointment, could not see anything. Paddy was looking ahead with the others and I went up to him. "Can you see the Andes, Paddy?"

"Sure, there they are just showing above the fo'c'sle head."

I had been looking low down on the horizon and was astonished to see the pencil line of the mountains so high up in the sky. I had never seen such lofty peaks before. Next morning, although the wind had been light and our progress slow, I gazed eagerly ahead at daybreak expecting to be able to distinguish conspicuous objects on the mountain side. To my utter disappointment, we did not seem to be the slightest bit closer than on the previous day. As I complained to the others, "one would think that the wretched mountains had been sailing away from us during the night."

It was fully three days after first sighting land that the Old Man decided to steer a northerly course. Our position was about fifteen miles south of Mollendo. All we needed was a breeze lasting two or three hours to bring our long passage to an end. Instead we lay rolling heavily to the long Pacific swell, our sails flapping so helplessly that the larger ones had to be hauled up to prevent them from chafing.

Now a greater anxiety began to assert itself. We were getting closer to the shore. Although we were drifting slowly northwards with the current, the big swell was also lifting us sideways. Restlessly the Old Man paced the poop hoping for a breeze. Apart from the oily swell, the surface was so devoid of ripples that the ship lay reflected in the water. And with the passing of each hour the shore was perceptibly nearer. Presently "Old Jowl" blew his whistle. "Watch stand-by to take soundings!"

"What's the idea, George?" I queried as we took the end of the lead-line from its roller on the poop for'ard outside of the rigging to bring it to the fo'c'sle head. "Surely, there's plenty of water beneath us? I've always heard that the sea is very deep off this particular coast."

"There's probably too much underneath us," answered George, "I expect the Old Man wants to find out if it is shallow enough to drop anchor. It's the only way to stop her drifting on to the beach, so far as I can see." Mr. Owen was waiting for us on the fo'c'sle head to secure the 14 lb. lead on to the end of the line. Although we had been to sea so long, this was the first time I had seen a deep-sea sounding taken. Already the men were standing on the ship's rail, about twenty feet apart, each with a small coil of lead-line in his hands. Mr. Owen "armed" with tallow the bottom of the lead, which was slightly hollowed, and when all was ready gave "Old Jowl" a wave. The mate waved back and, with a warning cry of "watch there, watch!" Mr. Owen flung the lead overboard. The sailor nearest him watched the coils slipping away from his hands in diminishing circles until, finally, as the last coil went without the lead touching bottom, he echoed Mr. Owen's cry to warn his neighbour that the responsibilty now lay with him. "Watch there, watch!" The cry was echoed by each man in succession until at length the line was running out through the hands of "Old Jowl" on the poop.

Suddenly it stopped. The mate bent over the poop-rail and jerked the line up and down to ensure that the nature of the sea-bottom would adhere to the tallow. Then he carefully read the marking on the line. "Ninety-six fathoms, sir," he announced to the Old Man.

"Ninety-six, eh? Well, we're within the hundred fathom line, anyhow. We'll take a sounding every hour," We tramped in the 192 yards of lead-line along the deck until finally the lead itself rose up to the poop-rail and, at the yell of "hold it!" from Mr. Owen, we paused expectantly. "Old Jowl" lifted the lead inboard and, having examined the tallow, reported "rocky bottom" to the captain.

"Watch there, watch. . . . Watch there, watch. . . ." We carried out the evolution four times and, with each sounding, the depth became less, but each time the shore was correspondingly nearer. We noticed too that, as the water shoaled, the big swell increased in height. Our last sounding had shown fifty fathoms, which was a questionable depth to hold a ship to anchor in such a swell, but the Old Man decided to risk it. The splash of the anchor, the rattle of the cable speeding through the hawse-pipe seemed like a death-knell to my hopes. For months I had been longing to hear that self-same splash, but then I had anticipated that the ship would be in Mollendo Bay, not off this waste of forbidding mountains with not a house in sight.

"Well, now that we're here, where are we?" queried Gogan jocularly as we adjourned to the half-deck after taking in all sail.

"The question is," answered Charlie, "are we going to remain here or are we to drag anchor? Did you notice that big swell breaking on the beach when we were up aloft?"

"I certainly did," I answered emphatically. "Seemed to break into big surf-curling rollers about a quarter of a mile out and then just race madly for the shore. I wouldn't give a ship much chance if she were caught in that lot."

"That's what I thought," George commented. "Still, we have the second anchor to let go if she doesn't hold with the first one. I didn't like "Old Jowl" saying that the bottom was rocky. There would be a better chance of the anchor getting a grip in sand." Suddenly there was a dull rumble and the ship vibrated throughout her hull. George paused for the noise to cease. "There goes the second anchor. Looks as though the Old Man doesn't feel happy about things."

142

Apart from an hour's individual anchor-watch which everybody had to keep in turn, we had all night in our bunks. At ten o'clock the following morning, which happened to be a Sunday, what we dreaded most happened.

Mr. Owen who was on the poop at the time was the first to give the alarm. The ship took a big sheer bringing the swell broad on the bow, and the anchors failed to bring her head-on again. Obviously they had broken their hold.

"All hands on deck!" How many times, I wonder, had we heard that familiar call since leaving Cardiff?

At the first warning cry from Mr. Owen, the Old Man came hastily out of the chart-room and summed up the situation at a glance. "We'll see if we can do anything with the kedge, Mr. Mate." He turned to "Old Jowl". "Put one watch getting the lifeboat over the side, and the other can get the kedge ready."

"Old Jowl" stumped rapidly to the break of the poop, took a deep breath and bellowed the order. There was never any mistake about what the mate wanted done. In calm or storm, the roar came from the depths of his lungs with equal volume and intensity. "Port—watch—clear—port—lifeboat—starboard watch—get kedge ready! You see to the lifeboat, Mr. Owen; I'll look after the kedge."

It was a forlorn hope from the beginning. The kedge is a light anchor chiefly intended for use in the calm waters of harbours or rivers to shift a vessel from one berth to another when she is without power. It is small enough to be hung over the stern of a row-boat by which it can be taken to a required position and then dropped, thus enabling a vessel to haul herself over to it by means of a rope or wire. In the days, too, before schooners had engines, they could sometimes be seen bound for sea, going stern-first down a river on a tide dragging a kedge-anchor underneath the forefoot. By such means the

143

vessel was kept under control and prevented from getting broadside on to the stream.

Captain Evans was faced with an entirely different proposition. In principle his idea was to drop the kedge-anchor ahead of the ship and heave her farther out to sea. He must have realized that, as the two big bower-anchors were refusing to hold the vessel in the heavy swell, such work with a kedge-anchor was bound to fail. He may have thought of the inquiry if the ship were lost. "Tell me, Captain Evans," some official at the inquiry might murmur, "did you not take any action to try and kedge your vessel clear of these existing dangers?" Possibly the Old Man, in anticipation, was taking no chances.

The preparations for kedging took up much time which, no doubt, seemed longer to us, in the increasing roar of the breakers. The wire strops holding the lifeboat in its chocks had to be released, and the canvas cover removed. The tackle-ropes for lowering away the boat had to be coiled down so that they would not become entangled. The boat had to be lifted, swung out, and the davits secured in an outboard position. She then had to be lowered and cork fenders held between her and the ship's side so that she would not bump in the heavy swell. Finally, when we did get her into the water we found that she leaked badly as she had not been afloat for months and her timbers had shrunk.

By the time we dragged her for'ard with the painter, leaping and swooping protestingly over the swell, "Old Jowl" had the kedge-anchor ready and hanging over the side. Here indeed was a dangerous job. At one instant the boat would be in the hollow between two seas ten feet below the ship's rail, then she would come soaring upwards threatening to put the kedge through her bottom to say nothing of injuring some of the crew. After one such escape, the boat was pulled farther for'ard and a long sling placed over the body of the boat, the ends of which were secured to the kedge. The kedge was then lowered away until it finally hung from the sling underneath the boat.

When the Egyptians built the Pyramids, they at least had the consolation that there would be something to show for their labours. The crew of the lifeboat had to row against the high swell hindered by a kedge-anchor hanging beneath the boat, but they had also to tow out the kedge-rope. With two men straining at each oar, the sweat streaming off their bodies in the hot sun, they fought gallantly for every yard gained. Further, their craft was only kept afloat by two men constantly bailing.

With the other apprentices and the starboard watch, I stood on the swinging fo'c'sle head watching the boat creeping slowly away. When the crew were about a hundred yards distant, it was evident that, through sheer weariness and the ever-growing weight of the trailing rope, they could go no farther. "Jowl," said the mate, "that's as far as they'll ever get," and, making a funnel with his hand, he yelled to them to let go. We could see Big Charlie whipping out his sheath-knife and sawing at the sling and, as the rope disappeared beneath the surface, we knew that the anchor had gone to the bottom.

"Right, men," said "Old Jowl", "take the rope to the cap-stan." Glad of action, we jumped to obey the order. Too long had we been standing idle listening to the sound of the surf growing louder, and watching the tell-tale vibrations of the anchor-cables. Clickity-click went the pawls of the capstan as we walked around. Alas, the rope was coming in too easily. It was obvious that instead of heaving the ship out of the kedge, we were heaving the kedge home to the ship. In less than half an hour it broke surface and hung dangling from the fo'c'sle head, its flukes shining like polished silver due to the friction of being dragged along the sea-bed. "Old Jowl" shrugged his shoulders and turned towards the poop. "Kedge-anchor hove home, sir," he called out to the captain.

I could see the Old Man shrug his shoulders resignedly. "Bring the hands aft, Mr. Evans," he called out, "and get them to clear the other lifeboat ready for lowering."

The other lifeboat? "Say," I said to George who was beside me, "what's the idea?"

"Blessed if I know," he answered, "unless he's getting ready to abandon ship."

"Abandon ship?" I exclaimed, "but . . ." I paused helplessly. "You're not leg-pulling, are you?"

George jerked his thumb significantly shorewards. "You can work it out for yourself. If the ship gets into that lot, nobody would survive. At the first couple of bumps the masts would come down, and I wouldn't like to be aboard trying to dodge 'em. The breakers in there must be over twenty feet high. They'd sweep the ship fore and aft, and then . . ." he left the rest to my imagination. My whole being protested. Better almost to be overwhelmed by the furies of Cape Horn, or to be hurled ashore on the Crocodiles than undergo this cold-blooded, ignominious ending on a fine and sunny day, only fifteen miles from safety.

Suddenly Gogan came up to us. "Do you know," he exclaimed excitedly, "I believe we are going to abandon ship! I've just seen the steward bringing up a pile of stuff from the cabin on to the poop, provisions, and gear belonging to the Old Man. What a lark! We'll all go home as D.B.S. (Distressed British Seamen) in one of the P.S.N.C. steamers. Plenty of grub and nothing to do. Why, we'd be home in six weeks!"

"Oh, shut up," growled George. "Here, give us a hand to get this boat-cover off." We worked at the boat in silence. I felt glad that George had shown his disapproval of Gogan's

146

viewpoint. It proved that I was not the only sentimental fool, as Gogan might have described me.

"Mr. Evans," called the Old Man, "tell Mr. Owen that we're not going to hoist his boat up. Tell him to stand off an' we'll beckon him alongside when we want him." Mr. Owen waved his hand in acknowledgement of "Old Jowl's" bellow.

Even as the ship dragged, there had always been the hope that the anchors might catch up as the water shallowed, but that had not materialized. A heavy lurch from the ship made me look around and I saw that a hill of water, much higher than its fellows, had thrown the bows of the vessel skywards with her anchor-chains taut and vibrating ahead. It passed down on each side of us as though its crest might break at any moment. Barely a cable astern, it toppled over and, in a seething smother of roaring foam, raced shorewards with spray rising above it in a smoky spume.

The Old Man watched it, his knuckles showing white under their tan as he clutched the taff-rail, and then turned to the mate. "Tell the hands to get that gear the steward has brought up into the lifeboat and then stand by to abandon ship."

Poor old *Denbigh Castle*! I glanced aloft at the towering masts and yards. How difficult to conceive that, within an hour or less when she struck, they would come hurtling downwards; that within seconds they would become a mass of tangled wreckage destroying the very hull which they had propelled right round the world. The words "abandon ship" were her death sentence, and to me it seemed as though some innocent person had been unjustly condemned. Surely, I thought, a reprieve must come from somewhere.

It came, and in the form of a reedy wail as though in protest against the Old Man's decision. It had a choking sound at times not unlike a man trying to clear his throat. Suddenly it stopped and, as though petrified, we stood gazing at one

147

another in astonishment. Again it started and, with one accord, we rushed to the starboard rail and looked out to sea.

A small antiquated-looking tugboat had rounded a projecting point of land and was coming towards us.

She was the most ugly-looking craft imaginable, in outline not unlike a crude child's toy such as might be seen in any huckster's shop. Her cigarette-like funnel was higher than her stumpy mast, and the paintwork on the rickety bridge was neglected and peeling from the heat of the sun. Even as we watched open-mouthed, the steam showed from her water-choked whistle, and once again we heard the reedy wail—a pathetic sound that would have brought grins and caustic comments from listeners in any British port, yet to us it was heavenly music. Ugly? To our eyes she had all the beauties of a millionaire's yacht. She was superb, majestic.

Almost unbelievingly we watched her struggling over a swell to disappear into the deep hollow when only her grotesque funnel and mast could be seen above the water. Next instant she would clamber into sight pushing foaming water from her bluff bows, giving the impression of a speed she could never possess. A figure on the funny little bridge took off his cap and waved. An unintelligible hail in Spanish floated across the water through a megaphone, which seemed to break a spell. "Old Jowl" came clumping down the poop ladder towards us, his face portraying an excitement which I never thought he possessed. "Get for'ard, all of you! Get that seven-inch hawser on to the fo'c'sle head and some heaving-lines," he rapped out with the precision of gun bullets. "Two hands down the chain-locker ready to stow cable; get that capstan connected up to the windlass, carpenter; come along, men, jump to it. There's no time to play around."

The little tugboat rounded up and maintained a position about twenty yards off our starboard bow. Her captain, a

148

swarthy little man with a fierce-looking handle-bar moustache which put "Old Jowl's" completely to shame, yelled orders to us and to his crew alternately. Sometimes he would rush off the bridge and, with hands raised above his head and eyes rolling wildly, engage in an excited harangue with one of his officers. We interrupted by flinging a heaving-line across his quarter-deck. A flood of orders came from his lips, and a substantial-looking tow-rope was secured to our line which we hauled aboard and made fast.

"Hold on, everybody!" The yell came from "Old Jowl". We glanced seawards as a mighty swell travelled rapidly towards the ship. Its crest reared upwards into an ominous narrow ridge which looked as though it could tumble over at any moment into terrifying surf. The bow of the *Denbigh Castle* soared as though lifted by giant hands. I glanced at the tug. She had just topped the summit and I could see a good third of her keel. We all whipped round and looked aft to follow the course of the sea. The deck lay in a steep hill downwards towards the poop, and I saw the solitary figure of the Old Man gazing anxiously upwards. As the swell swept amidships leaving the hull unsupported at each end, it tumbled aboard on both sides and, as though demented, the water rushed around the decks. Next instant our bow was swooping into a steep valley.

We clung desperately to our respective holds, dreading that she would strike bottom and that the masts would come crashing down in our midst, but she lifted again, still waterborne. Never had such a strain been put on our anchor-cables in that initial assault, yet, although they groaned, they did not snap. We found out later, however, that some of the links had been badly twisted.

A stream of vitriolic Spanish from the tugboat turned our immediate anxieties into amusement. Her captain kept darting from one side of the bridge to the other with astonishing rapidity, and at times would drum on the canvas dodger with his closed fists as though to emphasize his commands. A comical tinkle came from her telegraphs; foam boiled under her stern and she started to move ahead. Her crew stood on the quarter-deck paying out the tow-rope. How slender that tow-rope seemed when we thought that not only did many thousands of pounds' worth of ship and cargo depend upon its strength, but quite possibly our own lives. Fascinated we watched. Suddenly, when the tugboat was about a hundred yards ahead of us, the tow-rope rose clear of the water. It quivered like a fiddle-string, and flung off spray not unlike a dog shaking its coat after a swim. The *Denbigh Castle* gave a lurch forward and the cables slackened.

"Capstan, men, capstan!" bellowed "Old Jowl". We grabbed the big capstan-bars and, fitting them into the sockets, started tramping around. The pawls, or ratchets, which prevent a capstan going backwards with a weight, clicked merrily. Inch by inch the anchor-cables crept through the hawse-pipes and down into the chain-lockers where they were stowed in such a manner that they would run out without becoming entangled next time the anchors were dropped. Although the captain of the tugboat appeared to be a lunatic, he knew his job. Skilfully he manœuvred his little vessel so that we had only slack anchor-cable to heave in. "Roundy come roundy," as sailors say, and round we went until presently there came a check. The anchors were directly underneath us ready to leave the bottom. By now the vessel had moved out over a hundred yards seawards and, in consequence, the swell was not so high. "Lift 'em up, lads, lift 'em up! Let's get out of here." "Old Jowl" made a few circles himself pushing on a capstan-bar to inspire our efforts. With straining backs and feet slipping, we forced the capstan round until at length we knew

150

they must be clear of the bottom. "Old Jowl" made an "all clear" signal to the tugboat captain who acknowledged it with a toot from his whistle. Once again the tow-rope tautened and, in response to the strain, the *Denbigh Castle* started moving ahead. She was saved.

I looked at the tugboat, hidden at times by the black smoke issuing from her cigarette-like funnel, at the tow-rope which was pulling the *Denbigh Castle* seawards to safety and to Mollendo. Momentarily my thoughts reverted to fourteen months before when the tug was towing us down the Bristol Channel and I had longed for the moment when the tow-rope would be released. Now I would not have cared if we had a tow-rope tied to the ship all the way home.

CHAPTER ELEVEN

CAPTAIN HIGGINS

IT was November, and the *Denbigh Castle*, after having been one year, one month and twelve days on her passage from Cardiff, was anchored about two miles off Mollendo, and the mails had come aboard.

As I read my letters, the *Denbigh Castle* faded entirely from my mind. In spirit I was back home. There were numerous letters from my relatives and friends. There was also a pile of Christmas cards originally intended for the previous year but as it was now late in November, they were seasonable for the Christmas ahead. Daisy had by no means forgotten me. Her letters were full of ambiguous little phrases which made me long to see her and ask her what exactly she meant. Not that Daisy would ever tell you what she meant. Reverently I gathered up her letters and tied them together with a rope-yarn as we were short of fancy ribbon in the *Denbigh Castle*.

"What about tea, Paddy? You're the Peggy, aren't you?" The query from Charlie jerked my mind back to the present, and home, friends and Daisy Green had to be put back in their respective places, 8,000 miles away.

I went to the galley. "Evenin', Cookie."

"Evenin', young Paddy." Cookie handed me the pot through the doorway. "Did you hear the news about the captain?"

"No. What about him?"

"He's leaving the ship, look you."

"Leaving?" I exclaimed astonished. "And who's going to take his place? 'Old Jowl'?"

Cookie shook his head. "More's the pity. You could not find a better man whatever. A new man, a Captain Higgins, I believe, came on board but half an hour ago."

"What's he like?"

"Youngish, according to what the steward tells me. However, we will know all about him soon enough. Captain Evans is packing his bag ready to go ashore."

"I'm sorry to lose Old Man Evans," commented Charlie. "He's not a bad old skin really."

"Aye," remarked George, "I expect it's the sack for him, too. He's had a rough deal throughout the passage."

"Better a devil you know than one you don't," commented Gogan between mouthfuls. "Still, you never can tell. He might have a soft heart for apprentices and give us an extra whack of grub."

"That must be him!" I exclaimed. I could see the poop, and Captain Evans, accompanied by a stranger, had just emerged through the chart-room door. Eagerly the others craned their necks to get a view of the newcomer.

"Doesn't look like a captain," said Gogan, and we were inclined to agree with him. Aged about thirty-five, tall, with a slim, almost elegant figure, accentuated by a waisted jacket, reddish hair and moustache, he did not look like the sailing-ship masters we had seen around Cardiff. He tilted his homburg hat and, producing that symbol of snobbery, a white handkerchief, blew his beaklike nose.

"Could be a sort of Captain Kettle with his beard cut off," criticized George. "I'd say he's come out from home all right; he's not tanned enough to be living out in these parts."

Our deductions were abruptly cut by Captain Evans calling out sharply, "Half-deck!"

"Come on, lads," said George, and seizing our caps we shot out on deck and ran up on to the poop.

"These are the apprentices, Captain," said the Old Man. "Boys, this is your new captain, Captain Higgins," and he introduced us each by name. Captain Higgins did not shake hands, possibly because our hands were dirty, and he regarded us with disdain. We were not much to look at for, in addition to our dirty hands, our faces were none too clean, and our clothes patched and torn. "Hum," he turned to Captain Evans, "looks as though they could be smartened up a bit," and he dismissed us with a wave of his hand.

Mollendo. A few houses and huts, chiefly huts, stagnating at the apex of an apology for a bay, existing heaven knows how, on a coast as bare of vegetation as the Sahara. Except that it was an address for letters, that human dwellings were visible and that it was a good holding ground for the anchors, it seemed little different from the bay in which we had so narrowly escaped disaster the day before. After fourteen months of privation and hardship, I'd arrived at a destination which made the most lowly village in Ireland seem a little bit of heaven.

The morning after our arrival started with the usual routine carried out in port. The "yah, ha, yah ha" of the night watchman at five-thirty in the morning; the yawning, the tumbling out of our bunks half-asleep, the dressing into dungarees, the drinking of the vile liquid the cook called coffee, and then the six o'clock bellow of "turn-to," from "Old Jowl". There was plenty to do; gin blocks to be fitted and ropes rove through in readiness for the discharging of the cargo. Tarpaulins and hatches to be removed, stages to be rigged and rope-nets

154

dragged out of their locker. How I hated the sight of the sinister fuel bricks, recalling our streaming eyes and blistered skins. In the tropical sun, but seven degrees south of the equator, I had no doubt that these agonies would be intensified unless we took our previous precautions with the rancid grease from Cookie's barrel.

"Boys! Where are those dratted boys?" yelled the mate.

"Coming, sir!" and we ran aft to meet him.

"Get the long-boat washed out and have her all ready to row the captain ashore after breakfast. See that she's all shipshape, mind."

At nine-thirty sharp, in accordance with the mate's instructions, we had the boat alongside the accommodation-ladder leading down from the poop. She looked spick and span, as well she might, for we had scrubbed her, wiped her, scraped out specks of dirt from remote corners with our knives and placed a signal flag in the stern-sheets for His Highness to sit upon. Presently he came up on to the poop and, having given some instructions to "Old Jowl", stood looking down at us. We gasped. He was dressed immaculately in white drill and a panama hat. As he studied us, we knew instinctively that he was looking for some flaw. Descending the ladder, he climbed into the stern-sheets and, without even saying good morning, snapped out the necessary orders: "Push off bow . . . up starboard, back port . . . up together!"

I had always prided myself on my rowing, having spent most of my time in light boats or skiffs, when on holiday. The long-boat, however, was a different proposition. She was built for bad weather, stood much higher out of the water, and her oars were sixteen feet long. Before we were half-way ashore I was tired out. I had been pulling the oar towards my body with the strength of my arms instead of using my weight to lie back on the oar so that the real strain came on the muscles in the back. At the end of a week's practice, however, I found that the distance to be rowed was immaterial so far as becoming tired was concerned.

The Old Man steered us behind the shelter of a little pier or mole and alongside some steps. "You boys want a lot more practice. Go back to the ship and get a cleaner flag for the stern-sheets. Give those oars a good scrub. They are a disgrace to the ship. Shove off." He stood and watched us until we were clear of the mole.

"Tough guy, isn't he?" said Gogan pausing to wipe his face as soon as we had rowed a hundred yards or so. "Two miles in to the shore, two miles back to the ship, and then the same again, as though he were ordering a round of drinks. Eight ruddy miles before lunch. Not a bad beginning, I must say."

"Don't forget we've got to scrub the oars in between times," Charlie reminded him with a grin.

"Jolly good mind to ask him to let me work cargo instead," replied Gogan. "I thought this boat job was going to be fun. Instead, we're just galley slaves except that we haven't got an overseer with a whip."

Despite Gogan's pessimism the boat routine, while not exactly fun, was far from unpleasant as soon as we had hardened up our muscles. Apart from helping to wash down decks when we turned-to at six in the morning, it was practically a whole-time job. Usually, when we took him ashore after break-fast he would tell us to wait until he came down at one o'clock for his dinner. Often the Old Man would go ashore at seven in the evening and remain there until one o'clock the next morning. Never knowing on such occasions what time he would appear, we dare not leave the boat except for a walk along the mole. Often as not we fell asleep on the bottom boards. As he approached the steps, however, he always rapped out, "*Denbigh Castle*", whereupon we would leap out and light the steps with our hurricane lamp.

We took a personal pride in keeping ourselves tidy and our boat clean, and the day at last came when we could prove our efficiency at rowing. Besides the *Denbigh Castle*, there were two other sailing-ships lying off Mollendo, the *Westfield*, and one of our own Company's ships, the *Dolbadarn Castle*. On this particular morning the boats from the three ships left at exactly the same time. Our sense of competition was immediately aroused. As the other boats were manned by able seamen, and we were but apprentices, it would be a victory indeed to arrive first at the mole. As usual, Captain Higgins did not speak beyond issuing the usual orders, but we thought he seemed to give more concentration to his steering and occasionally he glanced at the other boats. As we approached the shore the boats naturally converged, and, to our mortification, we could see that the *Westfield* was about fifty yards ahead.

Up to the present we had been rowing with our normal timing but putting more weight than usual into our pulling. With but half a mile to go, George, who was stroke, said over his shoulder, "give her all you have, boys," and increased the rate by about five a minute. Our oars bent with the weight we put on them and the perspiration poured off our faces, saturating our clothes and wetting the thwarts upon which we sat. We dared not look around. Were we gaining or, dreadful thought, losing? Suddenly we discovered, by moving our eyes sideways, that our rival had come into our line of vision. Gradually we drew level, and then slightly ahead. Our hearts leaped within us for we could see by the manner in which they rowed that the *Westfield*'s men were obviously tired. So confident was George of victory that he eased his timing and, now rowing easily, we swung in behind the mole with a good lead of about forty yards. To our amazement the stevedores and longshoremen gave us an enthusiastic cheer. The Old Man apparently resented the demonstration from the shore and his face remained stern and immovable. Snapping out his usual order, "Wait here until I come back," he stepped ashore and walked quickly off along the quay.

Frankly we felt bitterly disappointed. One little word of praise, a "well-rowed, boys," would have made us feel fully rewarded.

"Well," and George mopped his brow, "no matter what the Old Man may think about it, we put it across both ships."

"Say," suddenly exclaimed Charlie, "is there anything lying on that flag in the stern-sheets, or am I seeing things?" We all turned around to look, and then became momentarily speechless. Glittering in the sunshine lay four half-crowns.

Our captain returned at about half-past twelve and George as spokesman, started to thank him for the present. Hardly had he spoken half a dozen words when the Old Man rapped out: "No talking in the boat! Up starboard, pull port!"

It was when I went along to the galley for our dinner that I learned some information which was both interesting and enlightening. "I hear," and Cookie shuffled with his pots and pans on the stove, "that you are great rowers in the boat, look you."

"How come, Cookie?" I queried.

"It is the steward who tells me he heard the captain talking to the mate. There was a wager on that race you had this morning."

"A wager?" I exclaimed.

The cook nodded his head. "It happened in the club-house ashore. Apparently our Old Man was talking with the other two captains about boat-rowing, and he told them that his boys could beat any crew they liked to put in their boats."

"You don't say!"

"The other two captains then laid a wager that the boat which came second would pay one pound, and the boat that was third should pay two pounds to the winner. So you boys cleared three pounds for the Old Man this morning, besides proving that he had spoken the truth about you."

Although my companions, when I hurried back and eagerly told them the story, showed an outward display of indifference, I knew that, like myself, they were jubilant. Indeed I think we were all more pleased than actually receiving the half-crowns.

CHAPTER TWELVE

BELAYING-PINS

ACCORDING to the terms of the contract made with the men we had shipped on board at Fremantle, they were entitled to be paid off as soon as the vessel reached the west coast of South America. "Old Jowl" had once again to carry out the job he detested, that of recruiting men. He had been successful in Fremantle and he did not come back empty-handed now. When he had exhausted the crimp-houses and the pubs, he visited the local calaboose and bribed the Governor to release some of his maritime captives.

I remembered with what a critical eye I had viewed our first crew when they had come aboard at Cardiff. They could have been called the sons of gentlemen compared with the new company, or "Old Jowl's Discoveries", as Gogan remarked. I received quite a shock when I saw the first head appearing above the rail as he climbed up the Jacob's ladder. He had a fierce-looking black moustache, a swarthy complexion, beetling eyebrows and wore gold ear-rings. Finally, he had a broad arrow-head branded upon his forehead. His nationality was doubtful but I imagined that he was of Portuguese origin. He had a name something like Gondaz, but we immediately christened him "Pirate". There were two Chillanos who looked like twins. They had powerful shoulders and stumpy legs, due probably to having spent a considerable part of their lives carrying saltpetre bags when loading ships. "Tweedle-dum and Tweedle-dee," commented George as they proceeded forward to the fo'c'sle, and the names stuck. They seemed immensely amused when they first heard their new titles, but afterwards they accepted the contractions of Dum and Dee without question. Even "Old Jowl" called them by nothing else. They quarrelled frequently and excitedly. It was not an uncommon sight to see them facing one another with eyes aflame, and holding their knives like daggers but with their wrists half-turned at their sides so that the blades pointed towards each other. Next instant they would sheath their weapons and embrace one another like the reunion of two schoolgirls, murmuring "*Amigo, amigo*".

One of the most fascinating of the new crowd was a wiry brown-skinned young man whose face was not unlike that of a monkey. His agility amazed us all. At sea, he could run bare-footed along a swaying topsail-yard without holding on to anything with his hands. At times he would make the men gasp by falling, or pretending to fall, yet in his descent he would catch the foot-rope and swing himself again on to the yard. On several occasions, when he was on a yard-arm, I saw him sliding down the leech of the sail (the edge connecting the two yards) instead of going in to the mast and descending the rigging to the next yard in the orthodox way. Even a gentle flap of the sail at the wrong moment could mean his being hurled to destruction and, on each occasion, he received a vigorous "blast" from "Old Jowl". We called him "Jacko".

As the days passed, we became anxious about those vital orders for home. It was through Mr. Owen that we first received the news. During our dinner-hour he suddenly poked his head through the doorway. "Hallo, boys; orders have just arrived that we are to load guano for Antwerp, direct! Just thought you'd like to know."

"Say, sir, that's good news. Thanks for telling us. And where will we load the guano?" asked Charlie.

"The Lobos de Terra Islands. They lie about nine hundred miles to the nor'ward."

Nine hundred miles? In reality, so far as distance at sea is concerned, it was but a short passage, but when we had to sail it in the opposite direction to home, it gave us rather a shock.

"We shouldn't take longer than a fortnight," said George, "possibly less. We should knock off five knots with the current. That's 120 miles a day or about eight days if we don't get becalmed."

"What are the islands like?" I queried. "Better than Mollendo, I hope."

George laughed cynically. "For a start, the islands are chiefly rock, sand and bird's muck. Nobody lives there, except the birds. The islands are closed to shipping for five years and become available for loading on the sixth. I've never been there myself, of course, but I've met lots of fellers who have. When a ship goes there to load, the Peruvian stevedores go and live there in tents until the loading is completed. There isn't even any water there, so they have to bring their own supply with them."

"Sounds mighty cheerful, I must say," commented Gogan. "And how do they load us?"

"They bag it and bring it out in lighters the same as they do here, but we have to discharge the lighters into the ship ourselves, and I believe it's a tough job with the lighters bucketing to and fro with the swell. Still, you get some fresh air. I've heard that chaps working down the hold can get gassed."

"Gassed?" I exclaimed. "What's this guano anyway?"

"Filthy stuff. Fertilizer, mixture of phosphorus and ammonia, and ammonia makes you choke."

Lobos de Terra. We arrived there one Saturday morning

after a passage of ten days, well within George's estimated fortnight. Despite the discouraging description, my heart sank as I viewed our second port of call, if one might call it such, to the west continent of South America.

Instead of a beautiful tropical island, I saw a grim, irregular-shaped hump of rock and sand absolutely bare of vegetation. Above and around it, myriads of sea-birds wheeled, uttering raucous cries as though angry at our intrusion. No golden-skinned dancing-girls, only a few rafts each holding two men who appeared to be catching fish. Finally, came the acrid smell of ammonia. One object, however, excited our interest—the four lofty masts of a barque showing between two sand hummocks at the other side of a point of land projecting into the sea. Apparently we were not the only unfortunate visitors to this desert island and we speculated on her name and nationality.

By now, all our sails had been furled and the ropes stowed neatly on their pins, so we adjourned to the half-deck for dinner. Suddenly Mr. Owen put his head through the door-way. "Captain wants the boat alongside at four bells this afternoon."

"Boat ready at four bells; aye, aye, sir," answered George.

"Well," exclaimed Gogan as soon as the second mate was out of earshot, "of all the dirty tricks! Here we are after a hard morning's work making fast all that sail, and we have to man the boat. What can he do ashore here, anyway? Build sand castles?"

"Expect he's going to visit that other ship," I answered with a sigh. We had never expected that the Old Man would want the boat and were looking forward to a free Saturday afternoon. There were clothes to be mended, shirts and dungarees to be washed, letters to be written or, for the lazily inclined, an hour in one's bunk having a quiet read.

Two o'clock, and we were waiting in the boat at the foot of the accommodation-ladder. Dressed in immaculate white drills, the Old Man descended and took his place in the stern sheets. "Push off." We did so, little realizing that it could easily have been the very last time we would push off. The Old Man did not steer for the shore but headed us towards the point at the other side of which lay the unknown barque. In a little while, as the point drew abeam about a hundred yards distant, the Old Man suddenly put the helm hard over and headed us out to sea.

Suddenly he spoke. "Some surf has broken to seaward of us. I don't suppose it's more than a solitary wave, as nothing has broken for fifteen minutes. We've got to keep the boat bow on to it. Watch your oars carefully and see that you don't lose them or let them jump out of their rowlocks. Keep your feet on the thwart in front of you so that you don't get thrown aft. Pull easy now, and as soon as I tell you to pull, put your backs into it."

"Aye aye, sir," we replied. A gigantic wall of water, whose ridge was so high that it toppled headlong into a welter of boiling foam, was moving swiftly, inexorably towards us. From the low level of our boat, it looked terrifying, and its angry roar increased. It looked like a wave that could engulf the world. As we rowed, we could not help glancing over our shoulders.

"Don't look round!" snapped the Old Man. "Just attend to your rowing." We kept our eyes fixed in front of us but our ears told of the rapidity with which this awe-inspiring wave was approaching. The roar became more thunderous, like a thousand cataracts tumbling headlong over a cliff. Anxiously we studied the face of the Old Man but his expression remained unchanged.

"Now, pull!" The command came like the crack of a whip.

We dug our oars into the water and almost lifted our backsides off the thwarts as we strained at the oars. The boat leaped ahead. Next instant our bow swung upwards . . . still upwards, until it seemed as though our little craft were standing on end. I looked downwards at the backs of George and Charlie who were first and second stroke and, together with the Old Man, they suddenly disappeared. Luckily I had both feet on the thwart in front of me, otherwise I would have been hurled into the stern sheets. As it was, the impetus lifted me right off the thwart. The noise was deafening. I could feel angry water rushing as high as my waist but could see nothing for the blinding spume. I clung desperately to my oar with a confused idea that, were I to be washed overboard, I would have something to cling to. Next instant our bow dipped and I had a blurred vision of the Old Man, emerging as it were from the sea, far above me. We had passed through the summit of the sea and were now sliding downwards on its opposite side as though into a bottomless pit. Was this, I wondered, our final dive? The boat straightened to a level keel and, with a quick movement, I wiped water from my eyes with my sleeve. The boat was practically full to the gunwale. Apprehensively I glanced at the next approaching swell, and, to my unspeakable relief, there was no break on its summit. I saw two sharks fins not more than thirty yards distant.

"Bestic and Gogan, keep her head on with the oars. You two start bailing." The Old Man spat out the words as he shook his head like a swimmer emerging from a dive. Immediately Gogan disappeared under the water in the stern sheets to reappear triumphantly holding the bailer which was stowed under the bottom boards. Charlie whipped out his knife and cut away the lashing which held a bucket under his thwart. In a trice he had the bucket free and was hurling the water over the side. George being equally busy with the bailer. As I saw that the water was rapidly receding and that we were no longer in immediate danger, the situation began to have its humorous side.

It amused me to see our debonair captain, his panama missing, his hair and moustache dripping with salt water, and his immaculate drills clinging to his body like an ill-fitting bathing-suit. It also tickled my sense of humour to see the two senior apprentices sweating like slaves as they bailed with all speed while I sat at ease just dipping my oar occasionally into the water to keep the boat's bow-head on to the swell. Presently, with the water swilling round our ankles, the captain ordered us all to resume rowing and we proceeded back to the *Denbigh Castle*. "Get the boat dried out," he snapped, climbing on to the accommodation-ladder. "And have her ready for me in half an hour."

By the time we had finished swabbing out the boat, our clothes had dried in the sun. In any case we had no time to change them as the Old Man boarded us punctually in the half-hour. This time he took the precaution of rounding the point a good half-mile distant and presently the other bay opened before us. Owing to the position of the point, it seemed to have a certain amount of shelter from the swell. A sudden muttered exclamation from our captain made us glance over our shoulders. To our surprise, the barque lay several yards from the shore. Her position was so strange that the Old Man actually spoke to us. "That ship is aground." Apparently the tide had receded for she stood upright and immovable although the water was swilling around her. Instead of proceeding alongside, we headed towards a creek lying at right angles to the bay. Moored alongside the small pier were two or three lighters used for bringing out the guano to any loading ship. There were also several small rafts from which the Peruvians were fishing.

"Can you see the name of the barque?" Captain Higgins queried.

George shaded his eyes with his hand. "Yes, sir. She's the *Stralsund*, of Christiana."

"Hum, Norwegian. Not like them to let their ship run ashore." He stepped out on to the pier and accosted two men, obviously Norwegian seamen, who stood at the top of the ladder. "Where's your captain?" he demanded.

One of the men touched his forelock. "He 'as gone to de mainland to see if he can get a tug. Our ship, she vos gone ashore."

"Yes," answered the Old Man a little sarcastically. "I can see that. Where's your mate?"

"De mate, he live aboard. We haf orders to live ashore. When de tide is in, de ship bump an' she is not safe. De masts may fall."

"Is there enough water to get alongside her now?"

"Oh, yes, sir. De tide is low but dere is plenty of water for your boat." The Old Man nodded and climbed back aboard us to give his usual formula. "Push off, back starboard! Pull port!" And we proceeded alongside the *Stralsund* where a Jacob's ladder hung from the quarter-deck. An elderly man with a bewhiskered face and no moustache peered down at us from over the rail. Gogan flung up the painter and, catching it dexterously, the man led it for'ard to sing out, "All fast".

Our captain climbed up the ladder and, as soon as he had disappeared down the companion-way from the poop leading to the saloon, we also clambered aboard. The bewhiskered one eyed us curiously. "What ship, mates?" he queried.

"*Denbigh Castle*," and George pointed to our masts showing above the sand-hills. "We arrived in here this morning."

"*Denbigh Castle*, eh? Well, see she doesn't go ashore. Proper death-trap this place is. Look at us, stuck in the sand and, so far as I can see, she's as much chance of gettin' out of it as if she was in the Sahara Desert."

"Who are you?" queried Charlie.

"Me? I'm the cook. I've been in this 'ere ship for close on ten years. The 'ands call me Gretchen; why, I don't know, an' I care less. Step into the galley an' I'll make you a cup of tea."

"You're not a Norwegian," I said.

"Not on your life. I come from Gosport, near Portsmouth, but give me the Norwegian ships before the British ones any day. They give you something to cook, which is more than I can say of the others." We stepped into a galley, bigger than ours, and undoubtedly much cleaner. The pots and pans, even the stove shone. "Hungry?" asked the cook.

"We're always hungry," replied Gogan promptly.

Gretchen nodded understandingly. "It's always the same in the English ships. No grub. Mean as ditchwater those Owners are. Hang on a bit, an' I'll see if I can fix you up with something." He opened a cupboard door and produced an attractive-looking piece of pork. "We killed one of the pigs last week," he explained, cutting off several rashers. "I bet you had only one pig when you left home, an' you killed it before you got to the Line, an' you haven't tasted a decent bit of fresh pork since. Am I right?" He placed the rashers into a pan, put it on the fire and gave it a shake. The aroma of the rashers, now starting to sizzle, wafted to our nostrils, and Gogan's eyes rolled in ecstasy. We bolted down a stupendous feed, at the risk of acute indigestion, partly because of hunger but chiefly through fear that the captain might suddenly appear and recall us to the boat before we had finished.

"How came it the ship went ashore, Gretchen?" I asked.

He shook his head sadly. "It happened only the night before last, Friday it was. Sort of freak wind came up from nowhere,

shortly after midnight. Hit the ship like a boxer's upper-cut,
it did. Her bow swung round, that quick so the night-watchman said, that her cable snapped across the stem, and away we
went careering towards the beach. The Lord knows the 'ands
turned out quickly enough an' we tried to let go the other anchor
but one of the cable-links jammed somehow or other in the
hawse-pipe an' next thing we knew she was bumpin'. How
the masts didn't come down I don't know. The riggin' must be
mighty sound. It was all over inside half an hour. Then the
wind and swell dropped and she seemed to settle down solid
into the sand. She still bumps a bit at high water, an' if we get
any swell out of the ordinary, she's finished. The Old Man is
properly het up over it, he's lookin' for a tug on the mainland but . . ." and Gretchen shrugged his shoulders expressively.

"Boys!"

"That's our Old Man," exclaimed George. Hastily we
thanked the old cook for his hospitality and climbed into the
boat. As we pulled away I looked with sorrow at the noble
vessel, like a sea-gull with a broken wing. How sad to think
that she might corrode away in this desolate place instead of
sailing triumphantly into her home port with a full cargo and a
voyage well completed. Incidentally, I never learned her
ultimate fate. We heard that her crew had been sent to Callao,
which looked as though all hope of her salvage had been
abandoned.

Next day was Sunday. We turned out at six o'clock as usual
but only to wet the decks down to protect them from shrinking
under the burning rays of the sun during the coming twelve
hours. We also put the long-boat into the water and cleaned
her out in case she was wanted. To ensure that she would not
bump against the ship's side, we rigged up a boom standing
out at right angles to the ship's rail and secured her to it.

"Well," said Gogan, as we sat in the half-deck eating our breakfast, "it might be that we get a free day today. It won't be that the Old Man wants to go ashore, and I don't suppose he'll be bothered visiting the *Stralsund* again."

"Suits me," I said. "Good chance for me to have a 'sailor's pleasure'." This term applied to the complete turning out of the contents of one's sea-chest.

"Not a bad idea," George commented. "My chest is about due for an overhaul."

This took us most of the fore-noon. After dinner we climbed on top of our bunks to read or sleep.

"Boys!" It was the voice of Mr. Owen, and he stood in the doorway to make sure we were aroused. "You're wanted." He turned a sympathetic deaf ear as we swung our legs over our respective bunk-boards and cursed.

"Yes, sir. Does the Old Man want the boat after all?"

"Not exactly," and Mr. Owen stepped into the half-deck, "but there's a bit of trouble afoot. It seems that some of the hands asked for shore-leave and the captain said, 'no'. Now we find that the long-boat is missing."

"Missing, sir?" we exclaimed together.

"Yes. Apparently they sneaked into her when everybody was having a Sunday afternoon's rest. The Old Man is furious, and he has told me to take the dinghy with you boys, find out where the long-boat is and bring her back to the ship. He intends to leave the men ashore for the night, and let them find their own way off in one of the lighters when they're bringing the cargo off in the morning."

We lowered away the dinghy and set off round the point. Mr. Owen made us feel important by asking if we considered that we were a safe distance off this dangerous corner. Certainly the sea looked safe enough, but we took no chances and maintained a distance of half a mile, as a boat the size of the dinghy would never survive the ordeal of the long-boat the day before.

"There she is!" exclaimed Mr. Owen as the *Stralsund* came into view. "The boat's tied up alongside the barque."

We glanced over our shoulders to see the small white hull plainly silhouetted against the black hull of the stranded vessel. "Won't the men kick up a shindy, sir, when they see us taking the boat away?" George asked.

"If they see us, no doubt they will; they might even try to stop us by force. The captain's whole idea is that we should try to take her away without being seen, or until it's too late for them to do anything about it. Should be an easy matter for us to slip quietly alongside, cut the painter and tow her clear of danger. Then we can row her back with the dinghy in tow."

Presently we were almost underneath the *Stralsund*'s bow. "'Vast pulling," Mr. Owen said in a sibilant whisper. "Unship your oars as quietly as you can and get your boathook ready. Hughes, you climb into the long-boat directly we're alongside and cut the painter. Cut it as high up as you can so as to save the rope." In a few moments, we were stretching out our hands to catch the long-boat's gunnel and we drew the two boats together. Swiftly and silently in his bare feet, George was aboard and started cutting the painter. Suddenly, with knife uplifted, he paused listening. The strains of a drunken song floated upwards from the saloon. We looked at one another with uplifted eyebrows. Mr. Owen, putting a finger to his lips, motioned George to go ahead with his cutting.

"Hallo, there! Is you boys comin' aboard to 'ave a leetle drink?" Startled, we looked upwards. Leering over the rail was Gondaz. He wore a cap made out of a red handkerchief with the corners tied together, and with the arrow-head on his forehead, the big black moustache and the gold ear-rings, he looked more like a pirate than ever. He leaned farther over the rail, and his genial expression changed as George suddenly came into view. "Say!" he exclaimed angrily, "what you play at? You try to pinch de boat, eh? We see about dat!" His head disappeared and the next instant we heard him bellowing to his shipmates, "Ahoy, you fellahs! Come on deck, queek! Our boat it is stole!"

"Hurry, Hughes," snapped Mr. Owen. "No time to lose! The others will be on deck directly, and who knows what might happen?" Even as George sawed through the last strand of the painter, we saw figures lurching and staggering on the poop and looking down at us from over its rail. A belaying-pin came whizzing through the air to miss George's head by about half an inch. Another and another followed but fortunately missed their mark. Next instant there was a concerted rush to descend the poop-ladder on to the main deck. Two of them tripped and fell, and the momentary delay enabled George to saw through the last strand of the painter and nip back into the dinghy.

"Push off!" Even for Captain Higgins we never pushed off so quickly as we did in response to that shout. Simultaneously our oars lashed the water and, with the long-boat in tow, we lay back on them with all our strength. A fusillade of belaying-pins came hurtling through the air from the main deck, but we were almost out of range and the aiming was poor. True, one coming farther than the rest struck Mr. Owen on the elbow but it was a glancing blow. Not until we were a good cable off did we cease pulling before getting into the long-boat and securing the dinghy to her stern.

"Well," said Mr. Owen rubbing his elbow, "I think we were lucky to get clear of that lot as well as we did."

"Tough guys," panted Gogan mopping the perspiration off his forehead with the back of his hand. "No wonder they were kept in jail in Mollendo. And where did they get the drink from?"

"No question about that. They broached the Old Man's rum cask."

"But the mate is supposed to be living on board," I interposed. "And then, there's old Gretchen. . . . I hope nothing has happened to him."

"Perhaps they did them both in," Gogan remarked excitedly.

"Ah, well," Mr. Owen rooted in his side pocket and produced a packet of cigarettes, "no doubt we'll hear about it later. It's no use us making any investigations." He handed round the cigarettes and ,we each took one gratefully. He nodded towards us, "light up". We had always liked Mr. Owen, but this little act exalted him still further.

"Right, give way," he ordered, as soon as we had finished our cigarettes, and leisurely we rowed back to the ship. The Old Man was pacing the poop when we came alongside. Through the open half-deck door I watched Mr. Owen making his report, and I saw an angry gleam come into the eyes of Captain Higgins. He nodded a dismissal to Mr. Owen and resumed his sentry-like pacing, planning, I had no doubt, a full retaliation on his misbehaving crew.

I turned to my companion. "I have a strong feeling that we are up against a whole pile of trouble if we start trying any tricks with this Old Man."

About nine o'clock that evening we were having a game of solo whist in the half-deck. Suddenly the sound of distant shouts, laughter and bursts of unfinished song could be heard floating in from the sea.

We all sprang to our feet. "Good Lord!" exclaimed Charlie, "that must be our crew. How did they get back?" We hurried out on deck. To our amazement, we saw a number of fishermen's rafts approaching the ship. Each had two of our crew paddling towards the ship. How they had rounded Surf Point, as we called it, without disaster remains one of life's mysteries. Obviously they were still drunk. They jumped for the rail and scrambled over it, some of them falling flat as they struck the deck, to be yanked, cursing and protesting, to their feet by those of their shipmates who could still stand up. They staggered slowly for'ard, pausing for long arguments on the way, until at length they disappeared through the fo'c'sle doors.

CHAPTER THIRTEEN

MUTINY

THE first sign of trouble was when Mr. Owen was thrown through the fo'c'sle door to land on deck on his back with his mouth bleeding. Having scrambled to his feet and spat a tooth into the scupper, he came aft, gingerly dabbing his face with a handkerchief, to make his report to the Old Man who, by accident or design, happened to be up at this unusual hour of six in the morning. Possibly, in view of the men's behaviour the previous afternoon, he intended giving them a talking to before they started work. He stopped pacing the poop with "Old Jowl" to watch the approach of the second mate. At the risk of a reprimand, we loitered as near to the scene as we dared.

"In trouble, Mr. Owen?"

"The hands refuse to turn-to, sir. When I went into the fo'c'sle to find out why, I was hit and thrown out."

Captain Higgins gave an almost imperceptible shrug of his shoulders, walked to the after end of the poop and came back again. "Hughes," he ordered, "go and round up the carpenter and the cook and tell them to come down to the saloon. You boys come, too." With a nod to "Old Jowl" and Mr. Owen, he went below.

We all went down the companion-way and paused outside the sacred precincts of the saloon doorway. "Come in, come in," snapped the Old Man impatiently. Caps in hand, we shuffled uneasily on the red carpet. He lowered himself into the swivel chair at the head of the table and seemed to survey us individually. One could almost follow his thoughts. "Old Jowl", a man of courage but handicapped by age and a gammy leg; the second mate, small but wiry; we boys, sturdy, full of enthusiasm, and fighting fit; Sails, not much good outside his own particular sphere of stitching canvas; the carpenter, under five feet in height but who advertised to all and sundry, "never be beat!"; the cook, decidedly ancient but possessed of hidden Welsh furies which could become fanatical; and, finally, the steward, lean, scraggy and undoubtedly out of training.

The Old Man lit a cigarette. "There's some trouble for'ard, you chaps, and, as Petty Officers of the ship, you've got to help me to stop it. I need hardly point out to you that not only does delay mean loss of money to the Owners but you are longer in getting home. I have a plan in my mind which I hope will solve the problem without much trouble. On the other hand, should it fail, it might mean a rough house. I take it that you are all prepared to stand by me?" There were murmurs of assent.

"You will excuse me for the minute, sir," said the cook. "I will not be away any time whatever."

The Old Man nodded, and the cook disappeared. Then, turning to Mr. Owen he asked, "Who hit you?"

"Gondaz, sir. He took me completely by surprise and then the others set on me and threw me out before I could retaliate. Had Gondaz and I been alone . . ."

The Old Man lifted his hand. "That's all right. We can assume that Gondaz is the ringleader." A knock came on the door and the Old Man called, "Come in."

Cookie entered and gave the captain what no doubt he intended to be a reassuring nod. Then, fumbling underneath his apron, he drew out his meat-chopper. Captain Higgins glared at him. "What the blazes do you mean by bringing that thing down here?"

176

"It was when you said that there might be a fight, sir. I always have it by me if I think there is any trouble, look you."

"Take that thing back to the galley."

"But indeed it is a very useful weapon, an' I always have . . ."

"Take it back, I said."

"Oh, very good, sir, but I always . . ." The cook disappeared up the ladder still muttering about the excellent qualities of his chopper.

"Now," said the Old Man, "my idea is to entice as many of the men as we can down here, one at a time, of course. Tie him up and gag him, and then drop him down the lazarette. Mr. Owen, you get some suitable line to tie 'em up with; rope yarns of a handy length should do."

"Very good, sir."

"And, Steward, we'll want rags of some sort to put into their mouths. Oh, and find something suitable to make gags with."

The steward scratched his head. "What about bandages, sir?"

"Heavens, no. We might need them later. Haven't you got an old sheet you could tear up?" The steward disappeared into one of the cabins, and presently we heard linen being torn. "You boys slip up on deck and arm yourselves with belaying-pins, then come back here."

"Aye, aye, sir." Excitedly we trooped out. "Say," said Gogan as soon as we reached the poop, "Mutiny on the *Bounty* isn't in it."

"I don't quite get it," Charlie remarked. "If we start scrapping with the Pirate and his gang, somebody's going to get hurt, even if we do win."

"The Old Man said something about taking on one at a time." I balanced a belaying-pin in my hand. "But I'm blessed if I know how he is going to arrange it."

Captain Higgins revealed his plan on our return. "The

idea," and he tapped an unlighted cigarette on his thumb-nail, "is that Mr. Evans goes for'ard and interviews Gondaz, tells him that I want to see him so that we can discuss the grievances of the crew, whatever they may be, and come to some arrangement. Hughes and Cowap, you stand on each side of the saloon doorway. When the man enters, Hughes hits him first with his belaying-pin. If he doesn't fall, Cowap gives him the second knock. Don't hit him too hard, just enough to stun him."

"Excuse me, sir, but how hard have I got to hit just to stun him?" George asked anxiously.

"How do I know?" answered the Old Man irritably. "Just use your own discretion." He turned to the steward. "Lift the lid off the lazarette and pull the ladder aside out of the way." The lazarette was a store-room under the floor of the saloon to which access was made through a trap-door. Its depth was about six feet. "Better see," he added, "that there are no hard cases in the way. I don't want any bones broken. Put a bag of sugar or something in the wake of the hatch."

"The bag might get busted, sir," the steward pointed out almost reprovingly.

"Well, put something else there then," snapped Captain Higgins. "Potatoes, anything. Use your common sense! Jump down, one of you boys, and give him a hand." Readily I obeyed. It was not often any of us had an opportunity of entering this particular domain of the steward where a tasty tin of fruit or salmon, kept exclusively for cabin use, might be slipped into one's pocket while his back was turned. The steward, however, kept a hawk-like eye on my movements. Having pulled a couple of bags of potatoes into the wake of the hatch and dragged the ladder to one side, I scrambled back into the saloon, the steward taking care that I preceded him. I could see the cocked eyebrows of my fellow-apprentices but, disappointedly, I had to shake my head.

"I guess we're all set," said the Old Man. "You can go for'-ard now, Mr. Evans, and get Gondaz aft. Don't go ordering the man about or you may arouse his suspicions. Speak to him friendly-like."

"Old Jowl" looked as though he would like to speak to him in any way except friendly-like. "I'll try, sir," he said, and went up the companion-way.

There was an atmosphere of tenseness, and my heart seemed to be beating faster than usual. I had made up my mind that if Gondaz was able to show fight after George and Charlie had dealt with him, which I doubted, I would bring him down with the flying tackle I had been taught by our Games Master at school.

The sound of footsteps overhead increased the tension. We all felt that much depended upon our initial efforts. George and Charlie, too, realized that upon them could lie the success or failure of the plan. Standing on each side of the doorway, trembling with excitement, they raised their belaying-pins as the footsteps drew nearer. The footsteps reached the top of the companion-way and then heavily descended the stairway. Next instant, Gondaz, bleary-eyed, stood outside the doorway with "Old Jowl" behind him to bar retreat.

"Come in, Gondaz." The Old Man lolled back in his chair with a sinister grin which, no doubt, he considered to be genial. "We're just going to have a little chat." Gondaz grinned in return and stepped forward. Perhaps it was fortu-nate for him that he did not trouble to remove his hat.

Thump! Gondaz staggered, but his hand darted behind to his sheath-knife. Thump! It was Charlie's turn this time, and with a grunt, the man fell heavily on to the deck.

"Tie him up now." The Old Man's grin was gone. "Make sure that you gag him properly so that he cannot warn the others." No fingers could be more skilled in making the knots to secure him, and presently we dragged the body to the open hatch and lowered it down, feet first.

"Let go!" ordered Mr. Owen. We heard the body thud on to the potatoes.

"So far, so good," said Captain Higgins with a nod of satisfaction. "Now you can tell me who were the men who attacked you, Mr. Owen."

"It's rather difficult, sir, as there was a bit of a mêlée, but those two Chilianos seemed well to the fore."

"Right. Get one of them along, Mr. Evans. Tell him that Gondaz wants to see him to consult him about terms. Don't mention me at all." Once again "Old Jowl" went for'ard to return presently with Tweedledum, like an old spider enticing a fly into his parlour. The sailor halted outside the doorway on seeing the captain apparently alone, sitting in his chair.

"Eh, where's Gondaz?"

"He's inside," answered "Old Jowl" truthfully. "Go on in."

Tweedledum, however, was suspicious. "Eh, Gondaz," he called out, "where are you?"

"Go in, I told you." There was a snarl in the mate's voice, and he gave Tweedledum a hefty push between the shoulder-blades. The sudden entry caught George by surprise. Thump went his belaying-pin but his aim was misplaced and landed on the victim's shoulder. Tweedledum gave a yelp of surprise then, realizing that he was being attacked, he backed out quickly with his arms protecting his head.

"Look out!" snapped the Old Man. "Don't let him get away!"

"Old Jowl", who still barred the doorway, had no such intention. Standing on his gammy leg and placing his hand on the bulkhead to steady himself, he met the posterior of the retreating figure with the flat of his foot and once more propelled him violently into the saloon. Eager to demonstrate my rugby tackle I hurled myself at his knees and we went down in a heap. A knife flashed from nowhere but the carpenter grabbed the man's wrist, twisted it and the knife fell. Old Cookie, despite the absence of his beloved chopper, threw himself into the fray and succeeded, at the expense of a bitten finger, in stuffing a lump of rag into the man's mouth just as he began to yell for help. Gondaz gave a grunt as his shipmate descended on him.

"Not so good," admonished the Old Man as we stood panting before him. "We'll dispense with the belaying-pins. Next time when Mr. Evans gives his last-minute push, Hughes and Cowap can each put out a foot and let him trip over them. Chips and Lawlor work the gag. Whatever you do, don't let him yell. The rest of you hold him and tie him up. Right?" He turned and nodded towards Mr. Evans. "Get his chum along. Tell him his shipmate wants him."

Tweedledee, in contrast to his predecessors, proved easy. He started to walk insolently through the saloon door and seemed so surprised at his reception that he had no time to put up much resistance. He gasped out, "Eh, what's . . .?" but Chips and Gogan did not even let him finish the sentence.

Thoughtfully the Old Man fingered his chin. "We must change our story now or the others will be getting suspicious. Tell them that an agreement has been made and that the captain is going to splice the mainbrace to celebrate the occasion. Impress upon them, however, that they must come aft one at a time. Got me?"

"Very good, sir." I thought "Old Jowl's" voice sounded rather grumpy. No doubt he was getting a bit tired of clumping up and down the companion-way and along the main deck. By this time we were becoming quite efficient in our drill, and three more men were captured without any unforeseen trouble. We waited for the fourth, but he never arrived.

"They've smelt a rat," said the Old Man after five minutes had passed. "Still, it doesn't matter. We've got the principal trouble-makers, and the rest will knuckle down without them. Let me see. Twenty hands for'ard, less six captured, less three neutrals, Big Charlie, Paddy and Taffy Jones, that leaves eleven, and our side can muster ten. Yes, we'll manage all right." Suddenly distant angry voices could be heard from for'ard.

"They're all coming now, sir," "Old Jowl" called down from the top of the companion-way.

"Very good, Mr. Evans, I'm coming up on deck." The captain motioned us to follow him and we all trooped up on to the poop. The men paused at the foot of the poop-ladder when they saw the Old Man, to say nothing of his bodyguard. He stood at the poop-rail looking down at them sternly. "Well, and what do you men want?"

"Where's Gondaz and the others?" a voice called out from the middle of the group. "And what about the grog?" cried another.

"Gondaz and the others are under lock and key," replied the Old Man blandly," and there's no grog." Suddenly his manner changed. "How dare you men come aft asking me questions?" he blazed. "Listen. Your leaders are helpless. Are you going to turn-to, or are you ready to have a free fight here and now? There are ten of us against your eleven." The men shuffled uneasily but nobody spoke. The captain removed his coat with deliberation, folded it and laid it on the cabin skylight. "I give you five seconds to answer me or else we're coming down to deal with you. What's more, after we've knocked the living hell out of you, I'll get you each five years in jail for mutiny, so make of your minds. One . . . two . . ."

The men started to mutter among themselves. They had no leader. Further, they had a heavy hangover from the night before. Finally, they knew the Old Man had the law on his side, and several of them were already acquainted with the extreme discomfort of a Peruvian prison.

"Three . . . four . . ." thundered Captain Higgins.

"Right, sir, we'll turn-to." Several voices hastily gave the assurance before the fatal word "five" was spoken.

Leisurely the Old Man turned and put on his coat, and the crowd, arguing amongst themselves, started to drift for'ard. "Stop! Stay where you are!" Startled, they turned at the yell of command. The Old Man turned to Hughes. "Slip below, get up the handcuffs and give them to Mr. Evans." In less than a minute George returned with the jangling bracelets. "Come up here, you," and the captain pointed to one of the sailors nearest to the ladder. The man obeyed and was promptly handcuffed by "Old Jowl".

A threatening growl of protest came from the hands when they saw what was happening. "Say, Captain, what does this mean? We said we'd turn-to, didn't we?"

The Old Man whipped round. "You stopped work against orders. Now you'll wait until I order you to start again, and in the meanwhile you'll wear these handcuffs. If you don't like it, you know what's coming to you. Come up here one at a time and hold out your wrists to the mate." Even to us, let alone the men, this was unexpected. We had all anticipated that, as soon as the lighters came alongside, everybody would start loading ship without any further trouble. Our captain, however, seemed to have different ideas. He turned to "Old Jowl" and Mr. Owen. "Take them down on to the main deck and handcuff them to the rigging and fife-rails or any convenient place. Keep them about ten feet apart."

"What about the loading, sir?" asked "Old Jowl".

"I'm cancelling the loading for today. First I must go ashore to the mainland and interview the British Consul. Don't release the men until I return. Now that I've got them where I want them I'm taking no further chances of a second mutiny."

"And when can we expect you back, sir?"

"Tomorrow morning. I see the steam launch which brings the mail and stores for the stevedores has arrived. I'll go to the mainland in her and return on the next trip."

"Very good, sir."

After the Old Man had gone, Mr. Owen came to the half-deck door. "When you've wet down the decks, boys, you can knock off work. But you've got to keep around the decks, watch the men, give them their meals and drinks of water when they want them." The wetting-down over, we sat down on the main hatch where the prisoners could be kept in sight, and discussed the situation.

We now experienced feelings of gloom. Mixing with the men, sharing in their hardships, aroused sympathy towards them rather than criticism. Even when the mate of the *Stralsund* visited "Old Jowl" and told him that a whole demijohn of rum had been stolen, we were inclined to make excuses on their behalf.

"Strikes me," George remarked, "that the Old Man carried things too far this morning. He calls them mutineers but we're not on the high seas. We're within the territorial limits of the Peruvian Government and the Old Man has taken the law into his own hands by handcuffing these chaps."

"Perhaps that's why he's gone ashore to see the consul," commented Charlie. "He wants to find out where he stands."

It was not until nine o'clock the following morning that the Old Man returned. To our surprise he was accompanied by a pompous little man, round-faced, clean-shaven and wearing a pair of gold-rimmed pince-nez. He had an attaché case in his hand. He gazed at the unfortunate handcuffed men in rather a bewildered fashion, and then followed Captain Higgins up the poop-ladder. The captain turned to "Old Jowl". "Release the prisoners and muster them aft."

The men, pausing on their way to rub their wrists and stretch themselves, shuffled to the break of the poop. A pathetic, spiritless crowd they looked with their unwashed, unshaven faces and red-rimmed eyes. To the newcomer they must have seemed a disreputable gang of ruffians indeed. Had Captain Higgins wanted any visitor to get such an impression, he had played his cards well. "You men," he said sharply, "this gentleman is the representative of the British Consul. I have reported your mutinous behaviour to him, and I want you to listen carefully to what he has to say as it affects each one of you personally." He turned to his companion. "Now, Mr. Halthorpe, if you're ready."

Mr. Halthorpe looked at the hands, wrinkled his nose as though in distaste, and then started fumbling in his attaché case from which he at length withdrew an imposing letter. "Men," he spoke in a high-pitched voice, "from the report made to me by your captain, I felt it incumbent upon me to draw up this letter, and after I have read it out to you I am placing it in his keeping. Ahem . . . 'It having been reported to me this 15th day of June by Captain Higgins, master of the ship *Denbigh Castle*, that the crew of the said ship did, on the 13th instant take leave without his orders; did board another vessel known as the *Stralsund* and purloin liquor for their own use; did on the 14th instant refuse to obey the lawful commands of the master or those of his officers; did assault one of the said officers, thus violating the Articles of Agreement to which they had attested their signatures or marks. Therefore, in accordance with the powers entrusted in me, I hereby authorize Captain Higgins to adopt any procedure which he may consider fit to quell any rebellious or riotous conduct among the crew which may arise during the remainder of the time they are under his command, and further,'" Mr. Halthorpe paused and looked at the men impressively, "'he is entitled to the use of firearms should he consider the necessity arises. Signed by my hand and witnessed,' etcetera, etcetera." He turned towards the Old Man and, giving a formal little bow, presented him with the letter.

"Excuse me, sir," said "Old Jowl", "but several of these chaps are foreigners, and if you ask me anything, they haven't the foggiest notion of what was in that letter."

"Ha! A very good point, Mr. Mate. Possibly it might be advisable for you to elucidate, that is to explain to them the gist of the letter in words that they can understand. No doubt you can do so better than I."

"Old Jowl" nodded, stepped forward and jerked his thumb in the direction of Mr. Halthorpe. "Listen, men. This hombre is a big noise from the British Government, see? He's told the captain in that letter that, if you stop work again, you can be shot, savvy? Now get for'ard an' stand by to discharge the lighter that's coming alongside."

Mr. Halthorpe raised his eyebrows, shuddered, and having shaken hands with the captain and "Old Jowl", proceeded rather hurriedly into the waiting launch as though anxious to be quit of the ship before any shooting began.

Thus ended the mutiny on board the *Denbigh Castle*.

CHAPTER FOURTEEN

END OF VOYAGE

A POUND of tobacco for the first man to sight the Lizard
Light. Like many other traditions of the sea this custom
has faded into oblivion with the passing of sail. When "Old
Jowl" passed the word, however, a wave of excitement went
through the ship, not because of the tobacco, although it was a
welcome present, but because the sighting of the Lizard meant
that the voyage was nearly ended. The flash from its 3,000
candle-power told everybody that England was but twenty-one
miles distant.

One hundred and twenty-six days had passed since we left
Lobos de Terra. Contrary to expectations the crew had proved
themselves to be a good sailing-ship crowd. The drastic action
of the captain at Lobos de Terra seemed to have been forgotten.
True, a steel marline spike had fallen from aloft on to the poop
about ten feet from where the Old Man was standing. Investigations had proved, however, that Jacko was the culprit
and, as he was obviously too irresponsible and lighthearted
ever to contemplate murder, he had escaped with a wigging
from "Old Jowl".

Captain Higgins had driven his ship and tested her crew to
the last ounce. There had been anxious days and nights when,
looking up at our over-canvassed yards, we felt that anything
might happen. The ship, however, was sturdily built and,
thanks to "Old Jowl", the gear up aloft was sound. She had
shouldered her way through racing high seas, her hull pounding

and shuddering in protest. Gales had shrieked through the rigging making the sheets and halliards groan and creak, but nothing had carried away. Throughout the whole passage, rising above any hardships, was the dominant thought that we were homeward bound.

The Chops of the Channel. With upper t'gallant sails set, passing less fortunate outward-bound sailing-ships shortened down to the strong westerly wind, towering above insignificant steamers plunging their bows into the head sea, the *Denbigh Castle* sped eastwards leaving a trail of white foam in her wake. By day, as the Channel narrowed, headlands rose out of the sea to greet her. By night, lighthouses flashed a welcome to this lonely traveller from far-away places. The ship sped onwards into the North Sea, past curtseying light-ships and bobbing buoys. Off the entrance to the Scheldt she paused reluctantly with canvas kicking as the main-yard was put aback to pick up the pilot and then, after a passage lasting one hundred and thirty days, she dropped anchor off Flushing.

Five o'clock the following morning we were all tramping around the capstan on the fo'c'sle head heaving the anchor up again. Never before had we hove up that anchor in such an exuberance of spirits. Never before had the pauls seemed to click so merrily. It was then that I heard for the first time that famous shanty, "Leave her, Johnnie, leave her", in which by traditional right the shantyman can express the opinions of the crew on the captain and officers.

Presently, like a prisoner under escort, the *Denbigh Castle* was conducted up the winding river of the Scheldt, past the dikes protecting the low-lying land, the picturesque windmills and the long Dutch barges so deeply loaded that the water actually lapped over their decks, until finally she was nosed through the gateways of Siberia Dock. In response to the pulling and pushing of the tugs she moved listlessly through the muddy water. Once alongside the dock wall she suffered the final indignity of being secured not only with wires and stout manilla ropes, but with heavy chains. She made no further movement, for her spirit had fled.

"Old Jowl" kept the men busy stowing away the spare gear, coiling up ropes neatly on their pins and giving final adjustments to the moorings so as to have an even strain on all parts. The time came when he stood tugging at his moustache, as though reluctant to utter the final words which would end the voyage. The hands eyed him expectantly and at length he spoke. "That'll do, men," and with a nod in their direction he started to stump his way aft.

"Hey! Mr. Jowl, sir!" The mate paused and looked round. Big Charlie was advancing towards him with an outstretched hand. Behind him came Old Paddy, Taffy Jones, the Pirate, Dum and Dee, Jacko and the rest. "You haf been a good mate to us, sir," said Big Charlie, "an' you vos a fine sailormans. We like to say gootbye."

The stern and rugged countenance of "Old Jowl" relaxed. No longer was he the mate, and these men, his crew. He was but a man amongst men, united to them by the bond of servitude to a mighty and exacting mistress, the Sea. He shook hands with each of them, addressing them by their nicknames practically for the first time. "Good-bye Big Charlie . . . good-bye Taffy . . . good-bye Pirate . . . take care of yourselves." He was parting with friends.

Having said their farewells also to Mr. Owen and us boys, the men, carrying sea-bags and suitcases on their shoulders, drifted along the wharf. Suddenly I heard a low whistle, and looking round saw that my old friend Paddy was standing on the quay beckoning to me. I was surprised as I had already taken reluctant leave of him.

He grinned. "There's some'at important I 'as to say to yer

189

that I couldn't say before the others. Tell me, are you still going to stay on at the sea?"

I hesitated. Swiftly my mind went over the previous two years. Should I go on another voyage, I would hold the exalted position of senior apprentice; there was a lot of the world yet to be seen, and finally I felt the call to "go down to the sea again, the lonely sea . . ."

"Yes," I answered simply.

"Listen." He laid his bag on the ground and put both his hands on my shoulders. "You've got to promise me some'at."

"Sure, Paddy," I answered lightly, "anything you say. You've been a wonderful shipmate."

"You've got to promise me," his fingers dug into my shoulders, "that you'll not make another voyage in the *Denbigh Castle*."

"What?" I exclaimed in surprise. "But why?"

He glanced swiftly around him as though afraid of some eavesdropper. "Because," and his fingers tightened again, "she's never agoin' to come back."

"Nonsense, Paddy." I smiled at him tolerantly. "Nobody could foretell a thing like that."

"I can." His earnestness was impressive. "I can't tell yeh how, son. I just know." A look, almost of apprehension, came into his eyes. "I can almost see it," he murmured as though to himself.

As I looked at him suddenly I seemed to become infected with his fears. Putting everything else aside, why should I not promise if only to please him? Had I not followed his advice for the past two years, sometimes against my own judgment, and always found him right? "I promise."

"Good lad!" Grinning happily, he clapped me on the shoulder. "Good luck, an' God bless ye." Flinging his sea-bag over his shoulder he lurched off along the quay with a typical seaman's gait. A pause at the corner and, with a wave of his hand, he was gone. I thought of my promise, and shrugged as though to shake off the fact that I might have been weak in yielding to an old sailor's superstition.

About a year later, when I was in a barque named the *Islamount* lying at Newcastle, Australia, memories of Paddy returned to me with such stunning force that I felt my face going white.

Having left the *Denbigh Castle* at Antwerp to go on leave, I had travelled to Dublin via Liverpool expressly to call upon Messrs. Robert Thomas to ask for a transfer to another ship. On stating my business to a clerk in an outer officer he had returned a moment later to say that Mr. Thomas could not see me and transfer was out of the question.

I put the matter up to my parents a few days after I returned home. "The only way to get this transfer," I had pointed out, "is for both of you to travel to Liverpool with me and demand a personal interview with Thomas himself."

"But why, dear?" Mother had queried. "What's wrong with the boat you're in now? You see, your father has had a lot of expense lately, and the fares to Liverpool . . ."

What could I say? Explain openly that I had made a promise to an old illiterate sailor because he had said that she was going to sink? Further, my parents must have some justifiable excuse for putting the request to Thomas.

"I must have the experience of a barque-rigged vessel," I had explained, if one could call it an explanation to poor Mother, to whom anything that floated was a boat.

Mother had sighed. "Well, dear, I'll try and talk your father into it."

So it was that, through the successful efforts of my mother, not only against the wishes of my father but against strong opposition from Mr. Thomas, I found myself in the half-deck of the *Islamount* twelve months later.

Our letters had just come aboard and I opened one from home. As I pulled out the letter the back page caught my eye. ". . . and to think," Mother wrote, "that, had we not yielded to your wish to be transferred to another boat, you would have gone down in her. Truly God works in a mysterious way. Your father wrote to Lloyd's Register of Shipping to try and get further news, and I am enclosing their reply."

With fingers that trembled I opened out the enclosure.

"Dear Sir,
"I beg to acknowledge the receipt of your letter of 20th inst. and in regard to the enquiry contained therein respecting the *Denbigh Castle*, I must regret to have to acquaint you that it is generally believed the vessel must have been overwhelmed in the heavy gale which prevailed in the English Channel during the early part of January.
"I am, Dear Sir,
"Yours faithfully,
"A. Scott, Secretary."

Paddy! I saw the wrinkle-faced little man standing on the quay-side, his sea-bag at his feet, his hands on my shoulders. "I can't tell yer how, son. I just know. . . ."